The Geological Society of America
Memoir 61

STRATIGRAPHY AND HISTORY
OF THE
MOENKOPI FORMATION
OF TRIASSIC AGE

BY

EDWIN D. McKEE

United States Geological Survey
Denver, Colorado

May 28, 1954

Made in United States of America

PRINTED BY WAVERLY PRESS, INC.
BALTIMORE, MD.

PUBLISHED BY THE GEOLOGICAL SOCIETY OF AMERICA
Address all communications to The Geological Society of America
419 West 117 Street, New York 27, N. Y.

The *Memoir Series*
of
The Geological Society of America
is made possible
through the bequest of
Richard Alexander Fullerton **Penrose, Jr.**

CONTENTS

ILLUSTRATIONS

PLATES

FIGURES

TABLES

ABSTRACT

The Moenkopi formation of Triassic age is composed of a series of deposits that form a wedge thinning eastward from a maximum of about 2000 feet in western Utah and southern Nevada to the vanishing point along an irregular margin in western Colorado, northeastern Arizona, and western New Mexico. Partly marine and partly continental in the thick western sections, it is entirely continental in the east.

Invertebrate faunas indicate that deposition began either during or preceding the middle of the Early Triassic (*Meekoceras* zone) and continued into late Early Triassic (*Tirolites* zone) and probably into Medial Triassic time. Vertebrate faunas also indicate an Early Triassic and probably, in part, a Medial Triassic age. Studies of the deposits indicate three major transgressions and three regressions across southern Utah and northern Arizona.

Analysis of sedimentary rock types and original structures in them suggests a complex mixture of environments involved in the development of the formation: stream beds, lagoons, playas, flood plains or tidal flats, shallow sea floors, and others. Some types are clear cut and readily demonstrated; others are open to question. Evidence from flora, fauna, and sediments indicates a semiarid to arid climate. Except for uplift in the Uncompahgre region of Colorado indicated by conglomeratic beds in the Moenkopi near by, the entire region probably remained very low and flat during Moenkopi deposition.

INTRODUCTION

Prior to 1938 paleontological evidence for the Triassic age of the Moenkopi formation had been obtained only from southwestern and east-central Utah where limestone members contain marine invertebrates. Elsewhere in the region a few isolated records of vertebrate remains and some scattered, fragmentary plant impressions from continental red beds constituted the only known traces of life and gave little precise information on the age of the enclosing strata. Dating of the formation over most of its extent, therefore, was on the basis of approximate stratigraphic equivalence of the Moenkopi beds in various parts of the region.

Since 1938 a sizable and significant group of vertebrate fossils from the continental deposits of the formation, especially along the Little Colorado River Valley, has been brought to light through careful searches by Dr. S. P. Welles and associates. The fauna includes remains of reptiles, amphibians, and fish. In addition, fossil footprints of distinctive types, first found by L. F. Brady (1935, p. 11) near Cameron, Arizona, and later collected in large numbers throughout the area and studied in detail by Peabody (1948), have added much to our knowledge of the life of the Triassic period in western America.

The present paper is a result of the recent discoveries of vertebrate fossils and the consequent renewal of interest in the Moenkopi formation. The study was undertaken at the suggestion of Welles and has a twofold objective: (1) to bring together as many data as possible bearing on the paleogeography of the time and the environment in which the vertebrate animals lived; (2) to check the age determinations based on a study of the vertebrates with those based on examination of marine invertebrates at various horizons in the formation.

To accomplish the first objective—a reconstruction of environmental conditions—

the writer has carefully reviewed the many local studies of the Moenkopi formation. Typical sections in nearly all parts of the region have been examined, sampled, and measured, and significant sedimentary structures such as ripple marks, gypsum beds, and cross-stratification have been studied in selected localities.

The second objective—the comparison of chronology in sections containing marine beds with that in sections composed entirely of continental deposits—has been attained through tracing of stratigraphic units. To accomplish this, advantage has been taken of the almost continuous exposures of the formation from east to west over a wide area. Beds extend from near Holbrook, Arizona, northwestward along the Little Colorado River to the type locality at Cameron, thence northward and westward along the base of Echo Cliffs and Vermilion Cliffs, respectively, and, from there, along the Virgin River Valley of southern Utah. By measuring a series of sections at intervals along this line of outcrop, sedimentary-stratigraphic evidence has been sufficient to demonstrate the relationship between the three major divisions recognized in the east and the six that appear in all sections to the west.

ACKNOWLEDGMENTS

This investigation has been conducted as a project of the Museum of Northern Arizona in Flagstaff, with the assistance of a grant from the Penrose Bequest of The Geological Society of America. The writer was ably assisted in both field and laboratory work by Halka Pattison Chronic (1946–1947), Otis Coulson (1947), Robert Ellsworth (1948), and L. F. Brady (1948–1949). He is indebted to Mr. F. G. Hawley of Tucson for most of the chemical analyses and to Dr. Siemon Muller for identification of ammonites. For helpful suggestions on the problem and criticisms of the manuscript he is grateful to Messrs. S. P. Welles, Frank Peabody, L. C. Craig, Edwin Colbert, John B. Reeside, Jr., and Stanislaw Poborski. Drafting of the geologic columns, done through the courtesy of the Museum of Vertebrate Paleontology, Berkeley, was by their staff artist, Mr. Owen J. Poe. Other illustrations are by David P. Willoughby and David Brodie.

GENERAL CHARACTER
DESCRIPTION

The Moenkopi formation of Early and Medial (?) Triassic age consists of a widespread, conspicuous series of strata unconformably above the Kaibab and other Permian formations and beneath beds of Late Triassic age. They extend throughout essentially the entire Colorado Plateau and occur in certain of the ranges to the west. In the colorful words of Dutton (1880, p. 144) these rocks (together with Upper Triassic beds above) "in some respects are the most extraordinary group of strata in the West, and perhaps the most extraordinary in the world. To the eye, they are a never-failing source of wonder." The features to which he refers are the brilliance and uniformity of coloring and the nearly unique expressions of sculpturing and weathering.

The Moenkopi formation is dominated by red and red brown. Many shades are represented, but over wide areas each is remarkably constant at a particular horizon. In the western part of the region, gray limestone is also prominent, especially in the lower half of the formation, whereas in many places white beds of gypsum contrast markedly with the dominant red. Also conspicuous, though of local distribution, are units of sandstone and mudstone that weather yellow or buff.

Topographic expression is a second distinctive feature of the Moenkopi. By and large, the rocks of this formation are among the weakest in the plateau province. Even where resistant limestone strata or massive beds of sandstone and siltstone constitute a part, the formation is unimpressive as a cliff-forming unit; it is, however, responsible for prominent benches or platforms that serve as treads in the great stairway of geologic formations in this region.

Because of contrasts in hardness between individual beds, and a general lack of resistance to erosion, the Moenkopi characteristically weathers into gentle steplike slopes that surround small mesas or extend outward from escarpment bases. In most areas, the slopes are cut by innumerable gullies and ravines that separate them into branching and tapering spurs. Low in the section, especially where crumbly mudstones predominate, the rock grades outward and downward into broad gently sloping plains, in places largely concealed by alluvium. High in the section, especially where the resistant overlying Shinarump conglomerate makes a protective cap, Moenkopi beds form weak cliffs or very steep, crumbly slopes. In such situations, prominent bands due to contrasting colors or the result of harder beds that form scarps are conspicuous and characteristic.

The Moenkopi formation, as currently defined, includes both marine and continental deposits that interfinger to form an intricate stratigraphic pattern. The marine deposits, mostly thin-bedded limestones and calcareous mudstones, are thickest and best developed in Nevada, northwestern Arizona, and western Utah. These areas constitute the western and northwestern margins of Moenkopi outcrop. On the other hand, continental red beds, consisting chiefly of claystones and siltstones and to a lesser extent of sandstones, constitute the entire section in exposures of eastern Utah and eastern Arizona, which are on the eastern margin. Between the two extremes is a wide area across north-central Arizona and south-central Utah in which the formation is composed dominantly of continental red beds but contains some strata of marine limestone and considerable amounts of bedded gypsum, probably of lagoonal origin.

The red beds of the Moenkopi are characterized by abundant sedimentary structures that testify to their accumulation on mud flats and deltas. Current ripple marks, exceptionally abundant, cover siltstone surfaces over wide areas. Cross-stratification, particularly of small-scale varieties, is moderately common in the coarser-grained detritals. Casts of salt crystals, rain pits, and other structures of subaerial origin are locally numerous, and the footprints of vertebrate animals are common at many horizons.

Concomitant with the lithologic change in Moenkopi deposits from east to west is an increase in thickness. Along the eastern borders of Arizona and Utah the formation is measured in terms of a few hundred feet and less. At the other extreme, in western Utah and Nevada it ranges between 1500 and 2000 feet. At the type locality on the Little Colorado River in Arizona, about midway across the State, it is approximately 400 feet thick. Unfortunately from the standpoint of illustrating the character of the formation, this section does not include all the members that are represented in the thicker sections to the west and northwest. Thus, for stratigraphic comparison the more westerly sections offer the best standards.

The studies of Reeside and Bassler (1922) in southwestern Utah and northwestern Arizona followed by the extensive work of Gregory (1948; 1952) and of Gregory and Williams (1947) across most of southern Utah have established a six-fold subdivision of the formation in that part of the region. The members, from oldest to youngest, are: (1) Timpoweap member, (2) Lower red member, (3) Virgin limestone member, (4) Middle red member, (5) Shnabkaib member, and (6) Upper red member. The Timpoweap, as defined by Gregory and Williams (1947, p. 226), includes conglomerates, limestones, mudstones. The Virgin member is gray limestone and calcareous mudstone, and the dominantly light-colored Shnabkaib is characterized by much bedded gypsum. Between these units are red-bed members that look alike and are largely siltstone and mudstone.

Gregory has indicated arbitrary boundaries between members of the Moenkopi formation because with one exception the contracts are gradational. In western Arizona and western Utah where the complete sequence of members is represented, these main subdivisions can readily be recognized through contrasts in lithologic character. Eastward, where only red-bed units occur, however, the difficult task of separating one member from another has been accomplished in large part by using key beds to determine lateral equivalents.

DEVELOPMENT OF NOMENCLATURE

The first geologist to observe the Moenkopi formation was Marcou (1858, p. 10, 11), who considered it Triassic and correlated it with the Bunter sandstone of Germany on the basis of lithologic similarity. Three years later Newberry (1861, p. 74) used the name "Red sandstone formation" of the "Saliferous series" for the same formation. He considered it Permian because of its position above limestone containing supposed Carboniferous fossils. Powell (1876, p. 54) introduced the name Shinarump group to include this and the two overlying formations, referring to the Moenkopi part as the "Lower Portion." Dutton (1880, p. 147) and Gilbert (1880, p. 6) used the same group name, but designated the Moenkopi as "subdivision 1" and as "unit C" respectively.

Following the discovery of invertebrate fossils then believed to be of Permian age, Walcott (1880, p. 221–225) separated the Moenkopi portion from the rest of the Shinarump group and referred to it as "Upper Permian." A similar designation was employed by Dutton (1882, p. 44).

The first two detailed studies of the Moenkopi, made at the turn of the century, were accompanied by proposals of formal names for the formation. Ward (1901, p. 17) suggested "Moencopie", and, apparently without knowledge of this, Huntington and Goldthwait (1903, p. 48) suggested the name "Verkin." A year later, Huntington and Goldthwait (1904, p. 203) dropped their original name and accepted "Moencopie" because of priority. This name has been continued by all later geologists but with a change in spelling adopted in 1916. Gregory (1916, p. 79) first used the present accepted form of "Moenkopi."

Names for subdivisions of the Moenkopi formation were first proposed by Reeside and Bassler (1922, p. 58) when the terms Shnabkaib member, Virgin limestone member, and Rock Canyon conglomerate member were introduced. All other groups of beds within the formation remained unclassified. Systematic studies by Gregory (1948, p. 225–226; 1952, p. 60) and Gregory and Williams (1947, p. 225) across a large part of southern Utah recognize the Shnabkaib and Virgin limestone members, re-define the basal member under the name Timpoweap, and recognize three other units termed upper, middle, and lower red members.

AREAL EXTENT

The distribution of the Moenkopi formation coincides in a general way with the extent of the Colorado Plateau in Arizona, Utah, and western Colorado. Precise limits of the formation in some areas have not been easy to define, however, and have been the subject of some controversy.

SOUTHERN BORDER: Southernmost exposures of the Moenkopi from west to east (Fig. 7; Table 1) are (1) in the vicinity of Lake Mead in southern Nevada (Longwell, 1928, p. 43), (2) near Black Point on the Walapai Plateau of western Arizona (Darton, 1910, p. 35), (3) along Sycamore Canyon south of Williams, Arizona (Price, 1949, p. 49), and (4) near the town of Snowflake in eastern Arizona (Darton, 1925, p. 204). Thicknesses determined at these localities are 1200 feet, 800+ feet, 330 feet, and 168 feet respectively.

Except possibly at the Snowflake locality, the southernmost outcrops of Moenkopi clearly do not represent an original limit of deposition in that direction. Thickness and especially textures in each of the outlier deposits indicate an original margin of the depositional basin considerably to the south. Near Snowflake, on the other hand, the Moenkopi is less than 200 feet thick and contains relatively coarse detrital sediment. A few miles farther south at Showlow (Darton, 1925, p. 204) it is absent, and Cretaceous strata rest upon Permian. Thus, if the Moenkopi originally extended farther south in this area, it was removed during pre-Cretaceous erosion and not during recent erosion as farther west.

EASTERN BORDER: The eastern limit of the Moenkopi formation coincides approximately with the Arizona-New Mexico boundary in the south and the Colorado-Utah boundary farther north (Fig. 7). These limits are at variance with those recognized in the early work of Darton (1910, p. 36) for he refers to the Moenkopi strata of considerable thickness in the Zuni Uplift, in an area northwest of Bluewater, and elsewhere in western New Mexico. His formation assignments in these areas are based on the occurrence of red beds above limestone strata of "Carboniferous" (Permian) age and below a conglomerate then believed to be the Shinarump.

A revision of the stratigraphy of the Zuni Mountain area by Baker and Reeside (1929, p. 1430) places the Permian-Triassic boundary at the base of the "Shinarump" of Darton and above the red beds because these red beds were believed too thick to represent the Moenkopi. These authors state that

"the true Moenkopi formation is thinning eastward (across Arizona), and since it is absent at Fort Defiance, Canyon de Chelly, and practically so on the east side of Monument Valley, it seems unlikely that the Moenkopi formation would, at a point east of Fort Defiance, have so great a thickness."

The red beds above the Permian limestone that Darton considered Moenkopi and Baker and Reeside considered Permian were found by Reiche (*in* Bates, 1933, p. 45)

TABLE 1.—*Key to Moenkopi measurements on isopach map*

Region	Thickness as recorded on map	Reference
Western Colorado	1120, 0	Dane (1935)
Eastern Utah	401, 370, 286, 0, 0, 0	Dane (1935)
Eastern Utah	637, 684, 626, 478, 451, 359, 368, 326	Baker (1946)
Eastern Utah	525, 375, 285, 450	McKnight (1940)
Eastern Utah	734, 840	Gilluly and Reeside (1928)
Eastern Utah	412	McKee (This paper)
Eastern Utah	460, 400, 200, 940	Baker (1933)
Southeastern Utah	325, 340, 254, 247, 167, 180, 130, 80	Baker (1936)
Southeastern Utah	222 (Comb Wash), 114 (Poncho House)	Craig (Personal communication, 1951)
Southeastern Utah	309, 160, 387, 384	McKee (This paper)
Southeastern Utah	302, 390	Gregory (1938)
Central southern Utah	514, 425, 304, 492, 540	Gregory and Moore (1931)
Western Utah	903+	Bacon (1948)
Western Utah	615+	Lee (1907)
Western Utah	470+	Maxey (1946)
Western Utah	1500–2300 (Sevier quad.)	Callaghan (Personal communication, 1951)
Southwestern Utah	1422, 1080, 1452	Gregory and Williams (1947)
Southwestern Utah	2150	Lee (1907)
Southwestern Utah	2035, 1775	Reeside and Bassler (1922)
Southwestern Utah	1533, 1762	Gregory (1952)
Northwestern N. Mexico	50 (Cheehilgeetho), 73 (S. of Wingate), 30 (Wingate), 0 (Zuni Uplift), 160 (Black Mtn. well)	Harshbarger and McKee (Unpublished sections)
Northeastern Arizona	0 (Carrizo)	Strobell (Personal communication, 1951)
Northeastern Arizona	0 (Lukachukai), 0 (DeChelly), 0 (Nazlini), 0 (Bonito), 130 (Klagetoh), 78 (St. Michaels)	Harshbarger (Personal communication, 1951)
Northeastern Arizona	175 (Black Creek)	Harshbarger and McKee (Unpublished section)
Northeastern Arizona	168, 82, 114+, 217, 250	McKee (This paper)
Northeastern Arizona	0	Darton (1925)
Northeastern Arizona	210 (Creager State Well)	Brown, Silas (Personal communication, 1951)
Northeastern Arizona	200+ (Kipling Petr. well)	Harshbarger (Personal communication, 1951)
Northeastern Arizona	175	Welles (1947)
Northeastern Arizona	123	Gregory (1917)
Northern Arizona	800+, 250+, 364, 336, 265+, 329, 296, 234, 324, 356, 441, 571, 433, 480, 561, 498, 465+, 198, 888	McKee (This paper)
Northern Arizona	481	Noble (1922)
Northern Arizona	330, 239	Price (1949)
Northern Arizona	389	Gregory (1917)
Northern Arizona	600	Ward (1901)
Northern Arizona	390+	Gregory and Moore (1931)
Southern Nevada	1598, 1221, 1634	Longwell (1928)
Southern Nevada	1500±	Longwell (1949)

to contain lithologic characteristics and petrified wood typical of Upper Triassic. For this reason they now are included in the Chinle formation, and the conglomerate above them, formerly designated Shinarump, is considered a member of the Chinle, high above its base. Recent stratigraphic work at Fort Wingate by John Harshbarger (Personal communication, 1951) has shown that in this area the true Shinarump conglomerate is 30 feet above the Permian limestones and that the 30-foot detrital unit immediately below it is Moenkopi.

The concept that Moenkopi deposits extend into northwestern New Mexico has recently been urged by Wengerd (1950, p. 71). He states that

"regional correlations, lithologic examination, and isopachous study of each formation [Moenkopi and Shinarump] carried into New Mexico from Arizona and Utah suggest strongly that Shinarump and Moenkopi beds are present off the northwest plunge of the Zuni anticline, and possibly throughout a great part of the deeper San Juan Basin."

On a map (p. 69) of the thickness of Triassic rocks he has marked "minimum easterly position," "optimum position," and "possible easternmost position of Moenkopi wedge edge," but he gives no specific supporting evidence.

The present study suggests that a combination of Wengerd's lines of "minimum easterly position" and "optimum position" most closely accords with available facts. The trends in thickness of the Moenkopi (Fig. 7) indicate an eastward thinning of the formation to less than 100 feet at St. Johns, Arizona (measured section, this paper), to 50 feet at the Cheechilgeetho well north of Zuni, New Mexico, and to 30 feet at Fort Wingate, New Mexico (measured section). Northward from this area the zero isopach contour swings westward into Arizona as shown by outcrops at Nazlini, Canyon de Chelly, and Lukachukai, where the Moenkopi is missing. Farther north it again trends eastward, passing into western Colorado.

Especially significant in indicating proximity to the eastern edge of the formation is the lithologic character of the Moenkopi formation at St. Johns and Concho where the formation is composed of a high percentage of medium to coarse detrital sediment in contrast to the progressively finer sediments westward (Fig. 12). Other red beds in New Mexico ascribed to the Moenkopi average much finer in grain size and are otherwise different from these marginal deposits.

North of the Arizona-Utah State line, the eastern margin of the Moenkopi swings northeastward into Colorado. The formation is present at West Creek east of Gateway, Colorado, and in Sinbad Valley, 10 miles south of Gateway (Dane, 1935, p. 43, 51). In this region it appears to have formed in an embayment that extended to the base of the ancient Uncompahgre highlands. Its margin is indicated not only by a northeast thinning of the formation but also, as pointed out by Dane (1935, p. 43), by an increase in that direction of coarse sand and conglomerate, including some large boulders.

NORTHERN BORDER: The northern boundary of the Moenkopi formation is located arbitrarily as deposits bearing other names but apparently equivalent in age and character extend far beyond the northernmost sections in which the name "Moenkopi" is used. Lower Triassic strata along the Green River (McKnight, 1940, p. 52), in San Rafael Swell (Gilluly, 1929, p. 83), in the Pavant Range (Maxey, 1946, p. 335), and in the Iron County Coal Fields (Lee, 1907, p. 364), representing an east-

TABLE 2.—*Age of Moenkopi formation*

Reference	Date	Name	Age	Evidence stated
Marcou, Jules	1858	"Trias"	Bunter ss.	Lithologic similarity to European Triassic
Newberry, J. S.	1861	Red sandstone formation (Saliferous series)	Permian	Stratigraphic position above supposed Carboniferous; lithologic character
Powell, J. W.	1876	Lower portion Shinarump group	Jura-Trias	Fossils of Howell examined by C. A. White
Dutton, C. E.	1880	Shinarump formation, Subdivision 1.	Permian or Lower Triassic	Position between Triassic and Carboniferous. Poorly preserved fossils
Gilbert, G. K.	1880	Shinarump group Unit C.	Jura-Trias	Position between base of Cretaceous and top of Carboniferous. Jurassic fossils by Howell in Uinta Mountains
Walcott, C. D.	1880	Upper Permian	Upper Permian	Invertebrate fauna and stratigraphic position
Dutton, C. E.	1882	Permian	Upper Permian	Fossils of Walcott at base; unconformity at top
Ward, L. F.	1901	Moencopie	Triassic	Conformable locally with Shinarump; constitutes part of one great series
Huntington and Goldthwait	1903	Verkin	Permian?	Accepts Dutton's designation
Huntington and Goldthwait	1904	Moencopie	Permian?	Accepts Dutton's designation
Ward, L. F.	1905	Moencopie formation	Triassic; lower portion probably Permian	Unconformably above Carboniferous; considered a conformable series with Triassic Shinarump
Lee, W. T.	1907	Moencopie	Permian?	Comparison of stratigraphic position and fauna with Walcott's Kanab Canyon sect.
Darton, N. H.	1910	"Moencopie formation"	Permian	General concurrence of opinion
Gregory, H. E.	1913	Moencopi	Permian	On basis of fossils of Walcott at Kanab Creek
Gregory, H. E.	1914	Moencopi	Permian?	On basis of fossils of Walcott at Kanab Creek

TABLE 2.—*Age of Moenkopi formation* (Continued)

Reference	Date	Name	Age	Evidence stated
Gregory, H. E.	1916	Moenkopi	Permian?	Fossils reported by Walcott from Kanab Creek and Permian plants from Quartzite Canyon
Shimer, H. W.	1919	Moenkopi	Lower Triassic	Stratigraphic position and faunal affinities
McKee, E. D.	This paper	Moenkopi	Lower and Middle (?) Triassic	Zones of marine invertebrate fossils, types of vertebrate fossils, fossil footprints

west line across central Utah, have been referred to the Moenkopi formation. North of this line, however, in Moffat County, Colorado (Sears, 1925, p. 284), in the eastern Uintas, Utah (Thomas and Krueger, 1946, p. 1259–1260), and in the central Wasatch Mountains, Utah (Williams, 1945, p. 477; Scott, 1950, p. 1530), similar strata have been assigned to the Woodside, Thaynes, and, in part, to higher formations. Farther west, in the Confusion Range, Utah (Bacon, 1948, p. 1045), and at Gold Hill, Nevada (Nolan, 1935, p. 42), Lower and Middle (?) Triassic beds, though clearly related, have not been given any formational designation.

It is not within the scope of this work to investigate details of the relationship between the Moenkopi and its equivalents to the north. Nevertheless, the *Meekoceras*-bearing beds in each are clearly parts of a once-continuous zone, and the red beds below this zone (*i.e.*, lower Moenkopi in San Rafael area; Woodside formation to north) are equivalent. It is not known as yet how many of the upper members and formations that occur in Idaho and northern Utah sections are represented in the upper part of the Moenkopi formation to the south.

WESTERN BORDER: The western border of the Moenkopi formation forms a north-south line across eastern Nevada. Thick sections at Goodsprings (Hewett, 1931, p. 34) and in the Muddy Mountains (Longwell, 1928, p. 43) indicate that the Cordilleran geosyncline in southern Nevada was sinking rapidly. Furthermore, the westernmost development of Moenkopi-type deposits was in that area.

In western Nevada and adjoining parts of California, as shown by outcrops at Candelaria (Muller and Ferguson, 1939, p. 1581–1586) and in the Inyo Mountains (Knopf, 1918, p. 84), Lower Triassic deposits are very different from those farther east and are considered to have formed in a separate, western trough (Nolan, 1943, p. 159). Deposition appears to have begun earlier in this trough than in the one to the east, but by the middle of Early Triassic time seas probably connected the two troughs, as shown by common occurrence of the *Meekoceras* zone. The western trough includes thick accumulations of volcanic materials but lacks the gypsum and red-bed deposits characteristic of the eastern trough.

MEASURED SECTIONS: Although strata of the Moenkopi formation are relatively weak and, therefore, tend to erode in many places as talus-covered slopes, nevertheless they are well exposed over wide areas in the Plateau province and are more accessible for study than many of the more conspicuous cliff-making formations of the region. A survey of the literature indicates that geologists have measured more than 60 sections of the formation in various parts of the region. In addition, 40 sections, many new but some representing remeasurements, have been measured as a basis for the present study.

VIEWS CONCERNING AGE

The age of the Moenkopi formation has been a subject of controversy for many years (Table 2), largely because, until recently, diagnostic fossils were not known from it. The formation was referred to the Triassic by Marcou (1858, p. 10, 11) and to the Permian by Newberry (1861, p. 75). Powell (1876, p. 80–81) and Gilbert (1880, p. 5) described it as part of a "Jura-Trias" group, dated partly on the basis of poorly preserved fossils discovered by Howell and partly because of position between the base of the Cretaceous and the top of the Carboniferous. Dutton (1880, p. 145) refers it to "Permian or Lower Triassic" for similar reasons.

On the basis of marine fossils discovered at Kanab Creek, Walcott (1880, p. 224) concluded that the formation was Upper Permian. Dutton (1882, p. 17) accepted Walcott's evidence, but Ward (1901, p. 29) called it Triassic because he believed it conformable with the Shinarump and part of one great series. Later Ward (1905, p. 19) stated that the lower portion was probably Permian. In contrast, other geologists who examined the Moenkopi between 1900 and 1919 inclined to agree with Walcott. Huntington and Goldthwait (1903, p. 48; 1904, p. 204), Lee (1907, p. 364), and Gregory (1913, p. 437; 1914, p. 494; 1916, p. 78; 1917, p. 22) referred it to "Permian?", and Darton (1910, p. 37) to "Permian."

Shimer's (1919, p. 492–497) study of the marine invertebrate fauna of the Moenkopi re-established belief in its Triassic age. Shimer concluded that deposition took place during Early Triassic time. All subsequent collections including those by Reeside and Bassler (1922, p. 59–62) and by Longwell (1928, p. 45–46), both of which were studied by Girty, and those of Gregory (1948, p. 227; 1952, p. 63) and Gregory and Williams (1947, p. 226) examined by Reeside, have confirmed its Early Triassic age. The discovery of the cephalopod *Meekoceras* in lower parts of the formation definitely establishes correlation of the basal part, at least, with the Lower Triassic Thaynes formation of Idaho, Wyoming, and northern Utah.

The vertebrate fauna in red-bed members of the Moenkopi also suggests an Early Triassic age but indicates that the uppermost part may be younger. According to Welles (1947, p. 286),

"the fish, the amphibians *Taphrognathus* and *Rhadalognathus*, and the reptiles are Lower Triassic, while the amphibian *Cyclotosaurus* is a Keuper form. In view of this and the general stratigraphic relations of the Moenkopi formation, it seems best that we refer it to the Lower Triassic, bearing in mind the possibility that the Moenkopi may extend at least into the Middle Triassic."

The trackways of vertebrate animals, studied by Peabody (1948, p. 413), further confirm the belief of an Early Triassic and possibly, in part, Medial Triassic age for the Moenkopi. Certain forms appear identical with Early Triassic types described from Europe, whereas others resemble Medial Triassic varieties.

Further information on the age of the Moenkopi is furnished by a collection of ammonites from the Virgin limestone member found by S. Poborski (Personal communication, 1951) near St. George, Utah, and examined by S. W. Muller. These specimens represent the *Tirolites* zone which is near the top of the Lower Triassic and considerably above the *Meekoceras* zone in the standard Triassic section. Because more

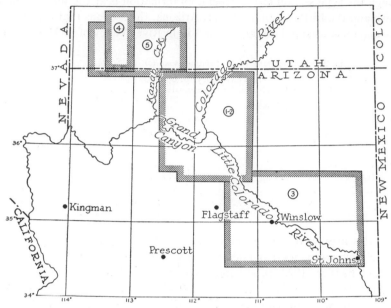

FIGURE 1.—*Index map showing location of series of sections in Figures 2–6*

than half of the Moenkopi formation, consisting of over 1000 feet of red beds and gypsum, is above this *Tirolites* zone, these upper deposits appear to represent not only highest Early Triassic, but also part of Medial Triassic time.

STRATIGRAPHIC TRAVERSE FROM SOUTHWESTERN UTAH TO NORTHEASTERN ARIZONA

GENERAL STRATIGRAPHY

Across southwestern and southern Utah, where the Moenkopi formation consists of alternating continental and marine deposits, distinctive lithologic members make correlation between sections relatively simple. Likewise, among the strictly continental deposits of the Little Colorado area in eastern Arizona, correlation has been accomplished on the basis of contrasting lithologic units. Between these regions, however, is a critical area of approximately 95 miles, across which the Moenkopi has not previously been studied and in which lie the clues to correlation between the well-established but different sequences to the northwest and southeast, respectively.

The clearly defined sequence of southwestern Utah is discussed first, next the type area and its southeastward correlatives in Arizona, and finally the intervening area. One of the main objectives of this study has been to determine through sedimentary stratigraphic methods the relationship of strata dated by marine invertebrate fossils to those dated by vertebrate faunas. The series of measured sections, which are the basis for conclusions concerning stratigraphic relations, are illustrated to scale in Figures 2–6, and their locations are shown on the base map (Fig. 1).

ACROSS SOUTHERN UTAH

Although the type section of the Moenkopi formation is at the junction of Moenkopi Wash and the Little Colorado River, Arizona, the sections that are most nearly complete and serve as standards are in the Virgin River Valley of southwestern Utah.

TABLE 3.—*Subdivisions of Moenkopi formation in Southwestern Utah*
(After Gregory, p. 60, 1952)

Member	Thickness in feet
Upper red	440–564
Shnabkaib	216–376
Middle red	436–520
Virgin limestone	8–116
Lower red	220–310
Timpoweap	80–230

Strata of this area were first examined in detail by Huntington and Goldthwait (1903, p. 48), who recognized and described five subdivisions in the Moenkopi. Later, Reeside and Bassler (1922, p. 60) modified these subdivisions and applied to the second and fourth, respectively, the names Virgin limestone member and Shnabkaib member. Recent work by Gregory (1948; 1952) and Gregory and Williams (1947) across a large part of southern and southwestern Utah has added much to our knowledge of the formation and has clarified the classification of members. Data presented here on the stratigraphic relations in that area are based largely on the detailed work of Gregory.

In addition to the five subdivisions originally recognized, Gregory (1948, p. 227) has described and named another; thus six members are represented in southwestern Utah. These subdivisions are not exclusive in lithologic character; each has some of the features of the others, and, with one exception, each grades into overlying and underlying members. On the other hand, these subdivisions are easy to separate at a distance on the basis of topographic expression, color, and dominant lithology, and they are recognized in all sections throughout the area. The members and their average thicknesses in the Virgin Valley are presented in Table 3.

The characteristics of the six members of the Moenkopi are brought out through analysis of two series of sections—one from east to west (Fig. 2) and one from north to south (Fig. 3). The two limestone members thicken westward and northward across southwestern Utah. Red-bed units also thicken westward, but thin northward in general. This thinning appears to be due in part to some deposition of limestone in place of detrital sediments in that area, but the upper red member may thin, in part, because of greater pre-Shinarump erosion northward. Characteristics and trends of each member are briefly summarized.

The Timpoweap member is described by Gregory (1948, p. 227) as composed of three unlike groups of strata: (1) conglomerates, (2) limestones, and (3) variegated shaly mudstones. It is the least understood and most inconsistent unit of the formation. It varies widely from section to section both in thickness and in composition. Much of this variation, Gregory believes, is due to the great topographic irregularities

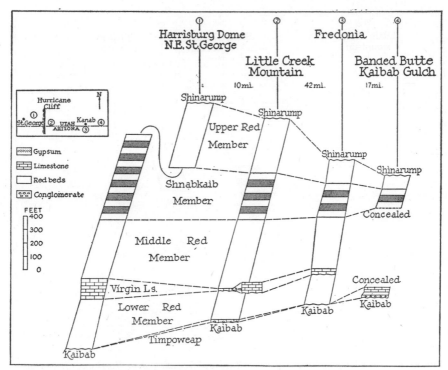

FIGURE 2.—*East-west series of sections of Moenkopi formation along Arizona-Utah border*

Data from Reeside and Bassler (1922) 1; Gregory (1952) 2; McKee (this paper) 3; Gregory (1948) 4.

of the Kaibab limestone surface on which the Timpoweap accumulated. Especially variable are the conglomerates at the base which appear to fill ancient erosion valleys and may have served to level off the region as the first step of Moenkopi sedimentation.

The gray limestones and yellow shaly mudstones that in most places constitute the uppermost beds of the Timpoweap member contain marine fossils, mostly gastropods, but include the cephalopod *Meekoceras* which dates the member as Lower Triassic. Although these beds definitely are assignable to the Moenkopi formation, observations by Reeside (Personal communication, 1953) indicate that the position of the formation boundary beneath them has not been satisfactorily determined for most localities. He states that some of the conglomerates commonly considered Timpoweap undoubtedly belong to the underlying Permian sequence and that the Kaibab-Moenkopi boundary, which represents a considerable time lapse as indicated by faunal evidence, is obscure and in many places. Concentrated work on both physical and biological elements doubtless will be necessary to determine satisfactorily the boundary in this area.

The Timpoweap member, as defined by Gregory, varies greatly in thickness. This is illustrated by his measurements of 13 feet at Little Creek Mountain and 452 feet

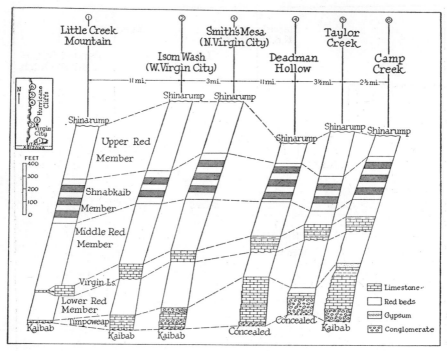

FIGURE 3.—*North-south series of sections of Moenkopi formation along Hurricane Cliffs, Utah*

Data from Gregory (in press) 1, 2; Reeside and Bassler (1925) 3; Gregory and Williams (1947) 4, 5, 6.

at Camp Creek about 30 miles to the north. As previously explained, however, considerable doubt exists as to whether all the deposits, especially in the thicker sections, should be classed as Moenkopi. The upper limestone-mudstone part of the member nearly everywhere weathers into a series of resistant steps.

The lower red member in most places is weak and slope-forming. It is largely red-brown shaly siltstone, some beds of which have flat surfaces, whereas others are covered with ripple marks. Structureless, crumbly red-brown mudstone likewise contributes toward forming slopes, but a few beds of resistant sandstone[1] form small cliffs or ledges. Gypsum lenses and veins are numerous. In Zion National Monument this member ranges in thickness from 200 to 370 feet (Gregory and Williams, 1947, p. 225), and in the Virgin River Valley from 220 to 310 feet (Gregory, 1952, p. 60). Throughout the member local erosional unconformities or diastems are reported at numerous horizons.

---

[1] Not examined for grain size; may be massive siltstone.

The top of the lower red member is marked by an unconformity that apparently has considerable lateral extent and is recognized in many places across southern Utah. Gregory (1952, p. 62) records 10–15 foot channels and irregularities from erosion in numerous localities. He describes a bevelling progressively southward and westward in Kanab Valley that accounts for a thinning of the lower red member of about 100 feet in 3 miles. Local angular discordance, accumulations of clay pellets, and irregular lenses of mottled shale are other features of the unconformity. The time represented by this break is not known, but its magnitude may be estimated by the presence of a *Tirolites* zone fauna (late Early Triassic) in the Virgin limestone above and fossils of the *Meekoceras* zone (medial Early Triassic) in the Timpoweap member below.

The Virgin limestone member is conspicuous throughout the southern Utah area as a moderately resistant cliff-forming unit between two weak, red-bed series. It consists of (1) gray, mostly aphanitic limestone in which the beds range from 1–2 inches up to about 3 feet in thickness, alternating with (2) calcareous shaly mudstones. Much of the limestone is clayey or silty, irregularly bedded, and weathers into small blocks. Its marine origin, and also that of the shaly mudstone, is attested by abundant invertebrate fossils, mostly pelecypods. This fauna includes the ammonite *Tirolites*. Because deposition of the Virgin limestone began on a surface of slight relief resulting from erosion of the underlying red beds, marked local variations in thickness are apparent. Nevertheless a regional trend in thinning of the unit is apparent, for it decreases eastward from 160 feet at Harrisburg Dome to 44 feet at Fredonia. Southward, a corresponding thinning is recorded.

The middle red member has a gradational contact with the marine Virgin limestone member below. The boundary is arbitrarily placed by Gregory where slope-forming, red-brown siltstones and mudstones are dominant over the more resistant, gray limestones and light-colored, calcareous, shaly mudstones. In general character, the middle red member is much like the lower red and is composed largely of thin, regularly bedded siltstones, many of them ripple-marked. Locally this member is gypsiferous and contains a few lenses of limestone, mostly near the top and bottom. It ranges in thickness (Gregory, 1952, p. 60) between 436 and 520 feet in the Virgin Valley but shows a decrease northward and eastward.

The Shnabkaib member, because of its conspicuous whiteness contrasting with the red beds above and below, is probably the most prominent subdivision of the Moenkopi formation. Its most characteristic feature is its gypsum that occurs as even regular beds, as lenses, in nodules, and in veins. Although some gypsum occurs also in several of the other members, nowhere else is it nearly so widespread nor abundant as in the Shnabkaib. Gregory (1948, p. 226) describes it in central Kane County, Utah, in "bands, commonly 6 to 20 in a series, and a few inches to 4 feet in thickness." In the Virgin River Valley, he (Gregory, 1952, p. 61) refers to the many gypsum beds that are regular for as much as a mile and that range in thickness from an eighth of an inch to 3 inches. Most of the remainder of the member is composed of olive-gray, gypsiferous siltstone and mudstone, some of which is shaly and some structureless. In eastern sections it contains one resistant unit of cross-laminated, gypsiferous sandstone near the top.

There are no definable boundaries between the Shnabkaib member and the red beds above and below. Olive-gray detrital sediments and deposits of gypsum occur in both subjacent and superjacent beds, forming a gradational contact. Boundaries are placed where red beds first appear dominant. The member ranges in thickness from 630 feet at Harrisburg Dome in the west to 250 feet at Fredonia and considerably less farther east. A few thin layers of limestone containing marine fossils are recorded (Gregory, 1953, p. 60) from this member in southwestern Utah.

The upper red member is in many respects lithologically similar to the lower and middle red members, but it contains a much higher percentage of thick, massive siltstones or fine sandstones that weather into resistant cliffs and ledges. Between these are beds of red-brown, shaly siltstone, many of them ripple-marked, and layers of crumbly, structureless claystone, both types similar to those that form the extensive slopes of the lower members. Gypsum is locally abundant; limestone and mud-pellet conglomerates are numerous as lenses, and some limestone beds are present. Gregory (1952, p. 60) emphasizes the "many lateral unconformities" within the subdivision.

Thickness of the upper red member is extremely variable. In the Virgin Valley it is listed by Gregory (1952, p. 60) as between 404 and 564 feet; in the Zion National Monument (Gregory and Williams, 1947, p. 225) as between 150 and 350 feet; in central Kane County (Gregory, 1948, p. 225) as between 98 and 130 feet. Some of the great differences undoubtedly are due to irregularities in pre-Shinarump erosion; nevertheless there is clear evidence of greater red-bed deposition in the Zion area than to eastward or to northward.

Differences in total thickness of the Moenkopi formation which are so apparent across the region probably are due to several factors: (1) unequal deposition in different areas during a particular interval of time, (2) progressively younger basal units eastward across the area, resulting from transgression, (3) progressively younger top units westward across the area, resulting from regression, and (4) removal by erosion of different amounts of sediment in different areas. The first three of these factors tend to give a wedge shape to the formation; the fourth, removal by erosion, was local and irregular in distribution and affects only two members—the lower red and the upper red.

Eastward thinning of the Moenkopi formation not only is manifest in the wedge shape of the formation, but also in the shape of each individual member (Fig. 8). Transgression clearly is responsible for thinning of basal members, but in certain higher members an accumulation of sediments that was more rapid in the west toward the geosyncline than eastward appears as a likely explanation.

Irregularities in thickness resulting from erosion subsequent to deposition both of the lower red and the upper red members are recognized in numerous places, but the total amount of sediment removed is not known. Gregory (1952, p. 62) shows that near Little Creek Mountains, Utah, the thickness of the Virgin limestone varies as much as 10 feet in less than an acre—the result of deposition upon a surface of relief—and that "in the Kanab Valley the redbeds are beveled progressively southward and westward, decreasing their thickness about 100 feet in a distance of 3 miles." Many illustrations of erosion having locally channelled, scoured, or removed entirely beds at the top of the upper red member also are recorded. This surface of erosion is discussed under the subject of Moenkopi-Shinarump Unconformity.

ALONG THE LITTLE COLORADO RIVER, ARIZONA

Stratigraphy of the Moenkopi formation along the Little Colorado River has been worked out largely by a network of sections examined and measured by the writer and his assistants during the summers of 1946, 1947, and 1948 and includes 7 com-

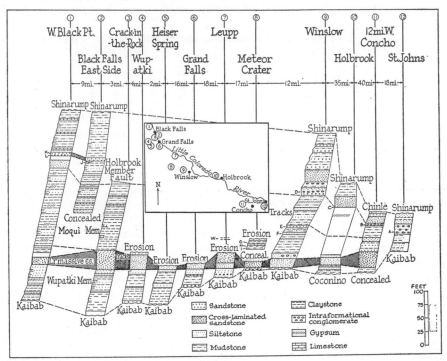

FIGURE 4.—*Northwest-southeast series of sections of Moenkopi formation along Little Colorado River, Arizona*

plete and 12 partial sections. These were not located at equal distances as might have been desired, although an attempt was made to have them as evenly spaced as suitable outcrops would permit (Fig. 4). Some of the sections were examined, regardless of spacing, because important vertebrate fossils had been found in these localities. Determination of the vertical and lateral extent of lithologic facies and the relationship between these and the incorporated faunas was emphasized.

Exposures studied along the Little Colorado River Valley extend from near St. Johns, Arizona, northwestward for 150 miles to the type section west of Cameron, Arizona. Although in this distance the formation ranges from 80 to 400 feet, the three subdivisions are readily recognizable throughout. As indicated by Welles (1947, p. 242), in the Holbrook-Winslow area, these units consist of an upper and a lower sequence of resistant, red-brown beds and a middle sequence of weak, gray to yellow beds that locally contain much gypsum. The contrast in color, together with the characteristic topographic expression (alternating cliff and slope, long gentle slope, alternating cliff and slope) makes these subdivisions apparent even at a considerable distance.

The lower subdivision of the Moenkopi in the Little Colorado region consists of an alternation of (1) massive, cliff-forming sandstones, (2) thin-bedded, ledge-forming siltstones, and (3) crumbly, slope-forming mudstones. Each is a shade of red brown. The most prominent single unit is a thick, rounded, cliff-forming sandstone, referred to as the "lower massive sandstone"; it can be traced across the area and is an excellent stratigraphic marker. Magnesian argillaceous limestones are locally

TABLE 4.—*Thicknesses of subdivisions along Little Colorado Valley*

Member	4.8 mi. W. of Cameron	Tappan Wash	Poverty Tank	Hwy. 89	W. of Black Pt.	Black Falls	Crack-in-the-Rock	Wupatki	Winslow	Holbrook	Concho
Holbrook (Upper)............	133	133	122	99*	118	138	...	...	114	45	25
Moqui (Middle).............	...	...	96	...	144	...	...	...	55	50	20
Wupatki (Lower)............	...	...	119	...	102	...	122	90	80	75	70

* Decrease due to pre-Shinarump erosion.

present at a few horizons as far east as Meteor Crater. Beds of conglomerate form the base in many places. They appear to have been accumulated in shallow depressions developed on the Kaibab limestone surface during pre-Moenkopi time and are absent where the relief of this surface was above average. Gravels in the conglomerate are mostly of Kaibab chert and limestone and are angular or subangular, indicating little transportation.

The middle subdivision of the Moenkopi in northeastern Arizona is similar in most respects to the Shnabkaib member of southwestern Utah. It is characterized by its general light color in contrast to the red brown of the units above and below, and it persistently forms broad benches or gentle slopes between the low cliffs of subjacent and superjacent beds. The rocks of this member include siltstones and claystones, most of them shaly or fissile, and gypsum beds, lenses, nodules, and veins. Strata are dominantly olive gray, though pale reddish brown is locally common. No fossils are known from this series of beds.

In the uppermost subdivision of the Moenkopi a series of massive, resistant sandstone and siltstone beds is responsible for the general cliff-forming character. Flat-bedded, shaly siltstones—many of them ripple-marked—together with brittle, crumbly mudstones form weak slopes between the cliffs. As in the lower subdivision, a dominant red brown prevails. Most of the resistant beds are fine- or very fine-grained sandstones, but some are siltstones. They are not only massive but tend to round off on the edges with weathering to form peculiar shapes responsible for the local name of "rock babies." Compound cross-stratification on a medium to large scale and abundant large cusp-type ripple marks testify to the fluviatile origin of these deposits. Reptile tracks have been preserved as casts on the bottom surfaces of these sandstones in many places, and amphibian skulls have been found in them. Other rocks in this series are limestones with irregular, discontinuous distribution eastward as far as Black Point, and intraformational conglomerates, most of which are formed of limestone or claystone pellets in a matrix of siltstone. Some of the limestones contain fresh-water (?) mollusks; others preserve fish plates and spines or isolated amphibian bones; the conglomerates contain worn and washed bone fragments, teeth, and traces of plant stems.

The three subdivisions of the Moenkopi in the Little Colorado Valley are persistent features of the area with definite trends in thickness as shown by Table 4. The upper unit was named the Holbrook member, and the bottom two, together, referred to as the Salt Creek by Hager (1922, p. 73). In this paper the term "Holbrook member" is continued, but the lower units are separated and named "Wupatki" and "Moqui." The present classification, therefore, is as follows:

Upper—Holbrook member
Middle—Moqui member
Lower—Wupatki member

A tentative classification by Welles (1947, p. 242) uses the names Lower, Middle, and Upper Moenkopi for the three members. However, as shown in the following discussion, all three are equivalent to the upper part, only, of the Moenkopi in sections of southwestern Utah. Furthermore, since these units do not correspond to "the lower, middle, and upper red members", respectively, as defined by Gregory and Williams (1947, p. 225) in the Utah area, a similarity in terminology might prove misleading.

Individual beds of the Moenkopi characteristically thicken, thin, and disappear in short distances along the strike, and many excellent illustrations of this may be seen in the Little Colorado area. On the other hand, certain groups of distinctive beds can be observed over wide areas. These are thick-bedded sandstone and siltstone units considered to be of fluviatile origin and to represent conditions of regression in which a blanket of sand was spread outward and westward from its source to the east. That such blankets correspond to time planes, except locally, seems doubtful, for the time required for their fronts to advance 50 to 100 miles must have been considerable. They occur progressively higher in the formation as one goes northwestward.

Most conspicuous and significant of the sandstone units or groups of beds in the Little Colorado area is the one referred to as the "lower massive." This sandstone forms a prominent cliff with rounded edges, in marked contrast to strata above and below, which make thin ledges or weak slopes. The individual beds of the sandstone are thick and, for the most part, cross-stratified on a medium to large scale. Texturally the rock is a *very fine-grained sandstone* ($\frac{1}{16}$–$\frac{1}{8}$ mm.) as shown by mechanical analysis of samples from 13 localities (Table 3).

The lower massive sandstone has a constant thickness in the southeastern half of the Little Colorado Valley averaging around 11 feet, but, from Wupatki National Monument northwestward, it increases progressively from 15 to over 50 feet (Table 5). From a stratigraphic standpoint, the corresponding westward thickening of deposits underlying the lower massive sandstone is especially significant. Aside from local, rather minor differences due to irregularities on the pre-Moenkopi erosion surface, it shows a constant and appreciable thickening (Table 5). This can best be explained as the result of regression, in which the front of the sand sheet became progressively younger as it advanced westward across the region, but other factors may contribute. This matter is taken up under the subject of Transgression and Regression.

TABLE 5.—*Thickness and position of lower massive sandstone, Little Colorado Valley*

	Moenkopi Wash	Poverty Tank	West of Black Pt.	Crack-in-the-Rock	1 mi. north of Wupatki	Wupatki	Heiser Springs	Grand Falls	Leupp	Meteor Crater	Winslow	Woodruff Butte	Sinks
Thickness......	53	34	35.5	36.5	28.5	16.5	..	11	11	10.5	14.0	11.0	5.0
Feet above fm. base.........	93	77	66	85	62	71	65	37	16.5	7.0	2.5	14.5	10.0

Other lithologic units in the Moenkopi likewise can be traced for long distances along the Little Colorado Valley, though none is so persistent or prominent as the lower massive sandstone. In the Holbrook member (upper red) is a limestone conglomerate containing many bone fragments, and also a massive sandstone bed that weathers into "rock babies," both of which can be recognized in numerous sections spanning many miles.

CORRELATION BETWEEN SOUTHWESTERN UTAH AND THE LITTLE COLORADO VALLEY

The critical area in a stratigraphic traverse from southwestern Utah to northeastern Arizona is the 95-mile interval between Cameron on the Little Colorado River and Fredonia on the Arizona-Utah border. Cameron is near the type locality of the Moenkopi formation and in the western part of the area that is characterized by a threefold subdivision. Fredonia is near the easternmost complete section that has the six members that are typical of all southwestern Utah localities.

To span the critical gap (Fig. 1) three possible solutions suggest themselves: (1) tracing key beds and lithologic units northward along Echo cliffs and thence westward along the Vermilion Cliffs of the Paria Plateau to House Rock Valley, (2) measuring and comparing a series of sections in various isolated exposures extending northwestward across the Marble Platform toward House Rock Valley, (3) measuring and comparing a series of sections in a line extending westward and to the south of Grand Canyon toward an area of thick sections comparable to those of southwestern Utah.

Tracing beds along the nearly continuous exposures of Echo and Vermilion Cliffs (Fig. 5) seems to be entirely satisfactory for establishing relationships between the two areas. Along this route are only two places of appreciable size in which the formation is not exposed—between Cameron and Gap Trading Post, and through House Rock Valley south of Fredonia. In neither interval do units critical for identification change character or disappear. The major problem encountered is that the route followed in tracing is indirect and circuitous, leading northeastward to Lees

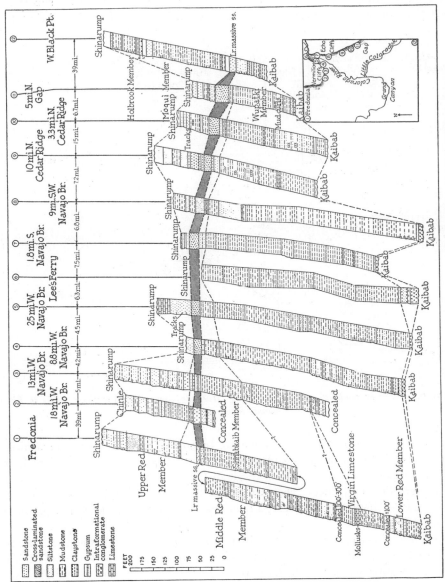

FIGURE 5.—*Series of sections of Moenkopi formation along Vermilion and Echo Cliffs, Arizona*

Ferry, then southwestward from it. As a result, variations in thickness of units in successive sections do not follow a constant pattern.

Northward from Black Point near Cameron, one definite trend in the succession of stratigraphic sections (Fig. 5) is a progressive thickening of red beds below the

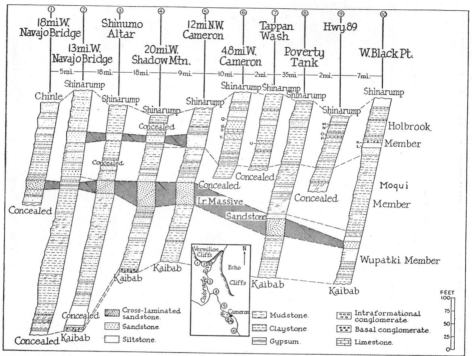

FIGURE 6.—*Northwest-southeast series of sections of Moenkopi formation, Vermilion Cliffs to Little Colorado River, Arizona*

lower massive sandstone. This sandstone can be positively identified and recognized across the entire area. It forms a blanket that must have advanced westward from the eastern margin of the basin as a result of little change in base level and consequent regressive conditions. The sandstone, therefore, is progressively younger toward the northwest, and at least part of the thickening of underlying deposits is explained as a result.

The Virgin limestone member, with its marine fauna, forms a wedge that may be considered to approximate a time plane (Fig. 8). Eastward across southern Utah it occurs progressively closer to the formation base and at some point east of Fredonia apparently is at the bottom. Thus, the deposits of the Wupatki member along the Little Colorado Valley appear to be younger than the Virgin limestone and probably are equal to a part of the middle red and much of the Shnabkaib members to the west.

A second definite trend in deposits of the stratigraphic succession along Echo Cliffs and Vermilion Cliffs is that the beds above the lower massive sandstone have a maximum thickness at the southeastern and northwestern extremes and a minimum near Lees Ferry in the middle, a feature best explained as the result of differences in amount of pre-Shinarump erosion. This variation in the amount of erosion

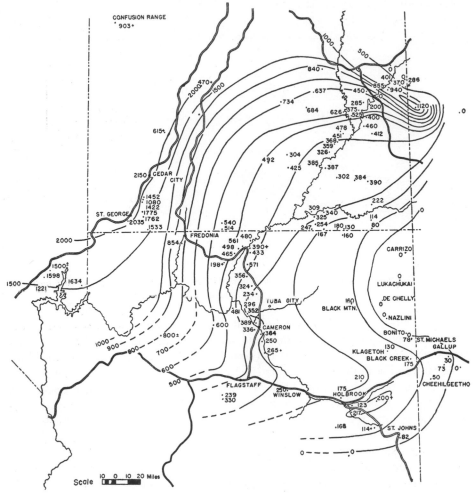

FIGURE 7.—*Isopach map of Moenkopi formation*
For sources of thickness data *see* key (Table 1).

may have resulted in part from an arching or doming of the central part of the region (Lees Ferry area) in post-Moenkopi time; in any event, marked local irregularities on the upper Moenkopi surface are noted across the area and are discussed under the subject of Moenkopi-Shinarump unconformity.

Data from the series of sections extending from Black Point near Cameron northwestward across Marble Platform (Fig. 6) corroborate conclusions drawn from the Echo Cliffs-Vermilion Cliffs series. Again using the lower massive sandstone as a datum plane, the lower red beds increase notably in a northwest direction, and the upper red beds are thinnest in the middle part of the area or at Shinumo Altar and west of Shadow Mountain. Additional evidence for correlation in this series is furnished by a distinctive upper massive sandstone that is recognizable from 12 miles north of Cameron north to Fredonia.

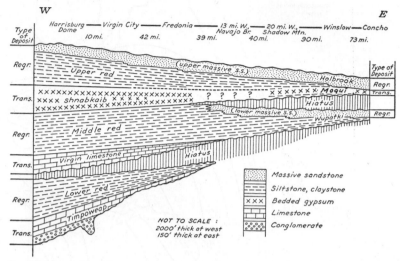

FIGURE 8.—*Diagrammatic east-west section of Moenkopi showing probable relations of rock units and hiatuses to times of transgression and regression*

Sections along a line extending from the Cameron district westward and to the south of Grand Canyon are few and have not been studied in detail. Measurements from Cedar Mountain, Red Butte, and near Black Tank (Fig. 7) indicate westward thickening of the formation, but trends within individual members are not known.

As certain rock units are reliable for correlation across the region, it is possible to establish with reasonable accuracy the relationship between the six subdivisions to the northwest and the three to the southeast. Superficial resemblances of color and topographic expression between members of the two areas have no significance. The middle red, Shnabkaib, and upper red members of the Utah section clearly do not correspond in detail to the Wupatki, Moqui, and Holbrook members of the Little Colorado area as one might easily suppose from general appearances. This is demonstrated by the lower massive sandstone that occurs in the upper part of the Wupatki member (lower red) at Cameron, but is high in the Shnabkaib member (gypsum) at Fredonia (Figs. 5, 6). Furthermore, the upper massive sandstone that marks the base of the Holbrook member (upper red) 12 miles northwest of Cameron appears high in the upper red member at Fredonia.

On the basis of correlation by limestone key units and through tracing sandstone blanket deposits, the Moenkopi formation of the Little Colorado region is considered equivalent to the upper portion only of the Moenkopi as represented in southwestern Utah. In brief, the Holbrook, Moqui, and Wupatki members are approximately equal to the upper red, the Shnabkaib, and an undetermined amount of the middle red member of the Moenkopi formation to the west.

MOENKOPI DEPOSITS OTHER THAN ALONG TRAVERSE
SOUTHEASTERN UTAH

Distribution.—Extensive outcrops of the Moenkopi formation occur in southeastern Utah. East of the Colorado River they have been described from exposures in the Monument Valley area (Baker, 1936, p. 40–44), along Comb Wash and in the upper walls of White Canyon west of the Bridges (Gregory, 1938, p. 47–48), in the canyon of Indian Creek and the vicinity of Moab (Baker, 1933, p. 34–37), and along the Salt Valley anticline (Dane, 1935, p. 42–54). West of the river, they are known from outcrops in the Circle Cliffs area (Gregory and Moore, 1931, p. 47–52), near Torry (Gregory and Anderson, 1939, p. 1843), in the San Rafael Swell (Gilluly and Reeside, 1928, p. 65–66), between the Green and the Colorado (McKnight, 1940, p. 52–62), and in the Green River desert-Cataract Canyon area (Baker, 1946, p. 54–58). During the present study, Moenkopi deposits in most of these areas have been examined and sections measured for comparison with the fossil-bearing strata studied in detail to the south and west. As yet only a few vertebrate fossils have been found in the Moenkopi formation of southeastern Utah, but an attempt is made to show the relation in time between these and fossils from Moenkopi beds of adjoining areas.

The isopach map (Fig. 7) shows that the Moenkopi formation thins toward the south and east across this region. As pointed out by Gilluly and Reeside (1928, p. 65), the thickness decreases from 850 feet on the west side of San Rafael Swell to 585 feet at Temple Mountain on the east flank of the Swell, and to 356 feet in Elaterite Basin farther east. These figures represent a west-east series along the northern area of outcrop. The same trend is clearly illustrated in the Monument Valley area, where Baker (1936, p. 43) obtained eight measurements showing a range from 340 feet at Monitor Butte in the northwest to 80 feet at Comb Ridge, about 45 miles farther east and south.

Continuing in the direction of thinning, Moenkopi strata are absent, apparently because of nondeposition, along a line close to the Utah-Colorado boundary in the south but extending northeastward into Colorado. The area of Canyon de Chelly and the Lukachukai Mountains in northeastern Arizona and that of the Rico Mountains of southwestern Colorado appear to have been land masses as far back as the beginning of Paleozoic time and to have acted as positive elements (McKee, 1951, p. 484). In Early Triassic time, as during most of the Paleozoic, an elevated area here probably contributed sediments to the region of deposition extending westward. Although direct evidence is lacking in many places because of the very fine texture and nondistinctive detrital materials, locally distributed coarse clastics in various marginal sections have contributed information. One source of sediments is considered by Dane (1935, p. 52), on the basis of an increase in coarseness toward the Precambrian rocks, to have been the Uncompahgre Plateau of Colorado.

Northwestward from the eastern border area of the Moenkopi, definite marine deposits, including fossiliferous limestones, occur within a red-bed sequence. The easternmost margin of these marine deposits in southern Utah (Fig. 8) is near Fredonia on the Arizona-Utah line, but further north it extends east of San Rafael Swell almost to Elaterite Basin on the Green River (Gilluly and Reeside, 1928, p. 65) and to a point near the junction of the Green and the Colorado (McKnight, 1940, p. 55). In southern Utah these marine deposits form the Timpoweap and Virgin limestone members, but in San Rafael Swell they are referred to as the Sinbad limestone. In the Circle Cliff area, due south of San Rafael Swell and between it and the southwestern Utah outcrops, no marine deposits are found.

Nowhere can the Moenkopi formation be traced from southeastern Utah to the type section along the Little Colorado River. Distances of 65 miles or more separate the nearest outcrop in one region from that in the other. Correlation, therefore, is based on: (1) lithologic similarity, (2) stratigraphic position unconformably above Middle Permian and below Upper Triassic deposits, (3) relationship of strata to fossil-bearing marine limestones, and (4) Early Triassic age of vertebrate fossils in both areas. Although upper and lower boundaries of the formation are in some localities open to question and the exact equivalence of various units in the two areas is not known, the broad correlation of the formation appears to be justified.

Sedimentation.—Throughout southeastern Utah the Moenkopi formation has the same general lithology that characterizes it in the type locality on the Little Colorado River and elsewhere to the south and west. In all sections examined it consists of three dominant types of rock, with lesser amounts of several others, locally distributed. The percentage of each type of rock varies somewhat from place to place (Figs. 12, 13), as might be expected, and contrasts with the percentages from other areas— probably the result of selective sorting with distance of transportation.

Of the three most abundant types of rock represented in the formation, two are pale reddish-brown siltstones. One of these is shaly, slope forming, and commonly ripple-marked. The other, which includes some sandstone, forms massive ledges, with weakly developed but large-scale cross-stratification. Locally it contains mud pellets or cavities once occupied by them, the bones of vertebrates, and large crescentic or cusp ripple marks. The third major rock type is a claystone, in part a mudstone (mixture of claystone and siltstone) that is brittle, crumbly, and structureless, weathering into tiny blocks and forming slopes. It varies from weak red to weak reddish brown, except where deoxidation processes have changed it to a light olive gray. This is the material in which most of the tracks of reptiles in the Moenkopi were formed, but because of the rock's crumbly nature they are seldom preserved in it. Nearly all known footprint records are from casts formed in covering layers of resistant siltstone.

True sandstones are uncommon in the Moenkopi of southeastern Utah despite repeated references to them in the literature. In the section at Indian Creek only one unit, a bed 5½ feet thick, was recorded. Likewise, near the mouth of White Canyon farther south (Fig. 9), only a single unit is recorded, though it is 49 feet thick. This unit appears as a conspicuous marker of pale reddish brown and can be traced eastward for more than 12 miles along the Canyon walls; it becomes progressively thinner and finally disappears. Eastward, in the Bears Ears section, virtually no sandstone is found, but to the south in Monument Valley thin sandstone beds are present at four horizons. All these sandstones in the Moenkopi are fine- to very fine-grained and are cross-stratified as a result of current action. Their relative scarcity in the formation is in marked contrast to the abundance of sandstones in the underlying Permian red beds.

Conglomerates in the Moenkopi formation are of two main types—those formed as basal deposits composed of fragments derived largely from an underlying Permian formation, and those developed as intraformational beds through the break-up of siltstones and limestones within the formation. Few deposits in the first category are found in southeastern Utah, probably because over most of the area the Moenkopi

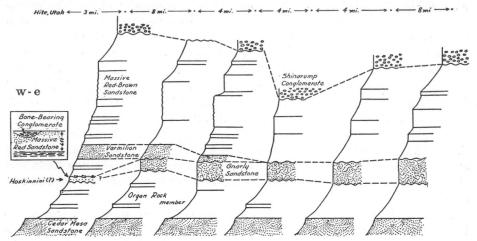

FIGURE 9.—*Sections along White Canyon, Utah, compiled from field sketches.* Estimated Moenkopi thickness 250–350 feet.

is underlain by friable sandstones and weak mudstones that disintegrated without forming gravels. Where conglomerates occur, as along White Canyon, the fragments are mostly clay balls and siltstone pellets. A notable exception is in the San Rafael Swell, where resistant limestones and cherts underlie the formation. According to Gilluly and Reeside (1928, p. 85), conglomerate beds have been developed in depressions of the erosion surface and locally in lenses as much as 20 feet above the base. Some of the gravels are rounded, but many are angular. Such deposits resemble those at the Kaibab-Moenkopi contact in many places along the Little Colorado Valley but are scarcely comparable to the extensive gravel deposits designated as the Timpoweap member in southwestern Utah.

Intraformational conglomerate of the type so abundantly represented in the upper member of the Moenkopi formation along the Little Colorado Valley occurs also in southeastern Utah. Here, as elsewhere, it contains bone fragments locally and indicates surface breakup, followed by limited transportation and concentration of debris. The fragments are largely calcareous siltstone or limestone pellets, and clay mudballs. Though not nearly so common as in most Arizona sections, these conglomerates occur in small lenses throughout the area.

Gypsum is not uncommon in the Moenkopi formation of southeastern Utah but, like intraformational conglomerate, appears to be less characteristic here than to the south and west. Its actual abundance is difficult to determine, however, for in many places it is concealed because of its nonresistant character.

Limestones are absent in the Moenkopi formation over a large part of southeastern Utah, but in the northern and western parts of this area they constitute an important member. In the San Rafael Swell they are thick-bedded, light gray and sandy, and range from 40 to 150 feet in thickness (Gilluly and Reeside, 1928, p. 65); along the Green River also they are present but much thinner (McKnight, 1940, p. 58). They form the Sinbad member of this region. Because of the occurrence in it of *Meekoceras*, this member is believed to be a correlative of the Timpoweap member of southwestern Utah. Extensive concealed areas prevent tracing between these regions, however, and precise stratigraphic or paleontologic data are not available. Limestone beds containing a molluscan fauna that has been examined by Girty are reported (Gregory and Anderson, 1939, p. 1844) from near Fruita, 25 miles southwest of the Swell. A few thin beds of limestone are recorded by Gregory and Moore (1931, p. 48) from still farther south, in Circle Cliffs. These limestones according to G. A. Williams (Personal communication, 1953) contain *Meekoceras* and are progressively thinner and lower in the section from north to south. He states that they are 50 to 75 feet above the formation base at Capitol Reef, about 15 feet above at the north end of Circle Cliffs, resting on the contact in central Circle Cliffs, and absent at the south end. Limestones are not recorded from Moenkopi sections east or southeast of those referred to above.

The abundance of primary structures suggestive of a continental environment has been noted many times in the red beds of the Moenkopi throughout southeastern Utah. By far the most conspicuous are ripple marks, common in the red shaly siltstones and also in the massive, cross-stratified siltstones. These marks are of two main types: a small, relatively parallel type (averaging 1 inch from crest to crest), developed on the surfaces of shaly deposits, and a much larger, crescentic type described as "cusp ripple mark," formed on the bedding planes of massive units. Both are typical of water-current action. Oscillation ripple marks are recorded by Baker (1936, p. 44) as also common in the Monument Valley area, but none has been observed by the writer. Other significant structures include mud balls and clay pellets common in massive siltstones; natural casts of salt crystals in shaly siltstones (Circle Cliffs Area) (Gregory and Moore, 1931, p. 48); shrinkage cracks in shaly siltstones, in some places superimposed on ripple marks; and rain-drop pits (Monument Valley area) (Baker, 1936, p. 41).

Nearly all geologists who have worked in this area agree that most of the red beds of the Moenkopi were deposited on a broad, flat flood plain that sloped gently toward the sea (west and northwest). The types of deposit, excluding the limestones and closely related beds, and the original structures in these deposits support this view. Some of the structures, as the abundant ripple marks, testify to current action in water; others, including shrinkage cracks and rain pits, represent times of exposure to the atmosphere. Gypsum and casts of salt crystals give evidence of evaporation, probably of local pools. The lensing character of many massive sandstone and siltstone beds and marked variations vertically and horizontally are in keeping with the concept of a flood plain.

In contrast to the evidences cited of continental deposition, there are in some parts of the formation criteria suggesting marine accumulation: (1) beds closely associated with unquestionably marine limestones, (2) long, even bedding planes, and (3) well-sorted detrital sediment. The validity of the last two appears to the writer to be highly debatable. Many of the deposits of fine sediment throughout the area have long, even bedding planes and show good sorting, yet all other evidences indicate that they are continental deposits. Possibly many of them, especially the claystones, were formed by settling in shallow ponds or lagoons. In brief, it seems doubtful that any marine deposits were formed in the southeastern part of the area.

In the northernmost exposures of the Moenkopi formation, in San Rafael Swell, the red-bed facies interfingers and passes into a very different facies composed of pyritic and carbonaceous shaly mudstone that is dominantly greenish gray. Gilluly (1929, p. 86) considers that these mudstones "are probably deposits of more or less stagnant, muddy delta pools" where much sulfur accumulated so that oxidation was inhibited, and he concludes that "all of the formation very probably is marine here." Similar gray, pyritic shaly mudstones are reported from Vermilion Creek in Moffat County, Colorado (Sears, 1925, p. 281, 284), from the south flank of Blue Mountain, Colorado (Gilluly and Reeside, 1928, p. 65), and in basal Moenkopi near Silver Falls Creek in Circle Cliffs, Utah (G. A. Williams, Personal communication, 1953). An alternative explanation of the color is post-consolidation reduction brought about by the introudction of pyrite in hydrothermal solutions.

SOUTH OF GRAND CANYON

Compared with the almost complete and nearly continuous exposures of the Moenkopi formation down the Little Colorado Valley, along the Echo Cliffs and the Vermilion Cliffs, and in numerous other parts of the region farther north, outcrops south of Grand Canyon are small and unspectacular. They consist of scattered outliers and remnants that have survived a general erosional stripping of Mesozoic strata from the southern border of the Colorado Plateau. They are significant for the information they furnish on areal extent and paleogeography of the formation.

Complete sections of the Moenkopi formation are recorded from (1) Cedar Mountain near the eastern end of Grand Canyon (Noble, 1922, p. 72); (2) Red Butte, 15 miles south of Grand Canyon village (Ward, 1905, p. 43); (3) near Cedar Ranch at the north base of San Francisco Mountain (Robinson, 1913, p. 26); (4) near the north end of Anderson Mesa, south of Flagstaff (Robinson, 1913, p. 27); and along the walls of Sycamore Canyon southwest of Flagstaff (Price, 1949, p. 51–53). Many partial sections have been noted in this part of the plateau, but the most significant is near Black Tank, 12 miles west of Havasu Canyon and 22 miles north of Seligman, recorded partly from outcrop and partly from well samples. It establishes the formational thickness in that area as greater than 800 feet and indicates the presence of the Shnabkaib and the higher red members that have been described from southwestern Utah.

Thicknesses of the Moenkopi formation ranging from 250 to 550 feet as found in outliers south of Grand Canyon (Fig. 7) indicate that originally this formation must have extended considerably to the south beyond its present limits at Sycamore Canyon and Black Tank. An increase southward in per cent of coarse detrital sediment, which accompanies a thinning in that direction (Price, 1949, p. 54), suggests that the source of the sediment was in the south.

SOUTHEASTERN NEVADA

Thick sequences of typical Moenkopi deposits occur throughout southeastern Nevada. In the Muddy Mountain and Virgin Mountain areas, sections measured by Longwell (1928, p. 43) range in thickness between 1000 and 2000 feet as follows:

Horse Spring Valley.. 1634 feet
Valley of Fire, west of Logan.. 1598 feet
Sandstone Spring, Boulder Wash....................................... 1221 feet

In the Frenchman Mountains near Las Vegas, approximately 2000 feet of Moenkopi beds outcrop according to Longwell (Personal communication, April, 1949), and 30 miles to the southwest, in the Goodsprings quadrangle, several partial sections measured by Hewett (1931, p. 32) indicate a correspondingly great original total thickness.

Detailed stratigraphic studies of the Moenkopi formation in Nevada have not been made, but representatives of most, if not all, of the six members recognized in southwestern Utah are present. At Goodsprings, Hewett (1931, p. 34) considers that the three units exposed in partial sections correspond with the lower red, the Virgin limestone, and the middle red members of the Utah area. The Timpoweap or basal member in southwestern Utah may be represented by conglomerate at the base of the Goodsprings section. More likely, deposition began there after Timpoweap development in Utah, for no basal marine limestone and no evidence of the *Meekoceras* fauna are known from the Goodsprings area.

In 1949 the writer accompanied C. R. Longwell on a reconnaissance trip to the Frenchman Mountains and Muddy Mountains, where complete sections of Moenkopi formation are exposed. Not only could the lower and middle red and the Virgin limestone members be recognized easily in these areas, but also the Shnabkaib and upper red members. As at Goodsprings, no *Meekoceras*-bearing beds were found at the base, though a conglomerate of variable thickness may represent the Timpoweap member.

The thickness of the Moenkopi formation in southeastern Nevada indicates clearly that here, as in southwestern Utah, it developed in an area of rapid sinking. Sedimentation during the Lower Triassic epoch probably began in this area at or soon after the time represented by the *Meekoceras* fauna, but marine deposition did not start until somewhat later when the Virgin limestone had begun to form.

Nolan (1943, p. 158) considers that the region of southeastern Nevada was part of an eastern depositional trough, separated from another to the west that occupied central and western Nevada during Early Triassic time. He points out, furthermore, that the large amount of gypsum in the Moenkopi of the southeastern Nevada area indicates that the trough had no outlet to the south but that salines and other lagoonal deposits accumulated along the southern margins of the sea. In the Virgin Mountains and Muddy Mountains, thick lenticular beds of gypsum occur in both the Shnabkiab and the lower red members.

Evidence of a barrier west of the southeastern Nevada trough has been recorded by Hewett (1931, p. 33), who describes "well rounded cobbles" most of which range from 3 to 6 inches and rarely up to 10 inches in diameter in the upper part of Moenkopi section at Goodsprings. These gravels are derived from trachyte flows and indurated breccias. Also present is a greenish-gray tuff, indicating volcanic activity, possibly related to that which was responsible for extensive tuffaceous deposits in the western trough (Muller and Ferguson, 1939).

How far south from southeastern Nevada the deposition of Moenkopi sediments extended is not known. Lower Triassic beds, totalling about 1000 feet thick, have been reported from the Providence Mountains, California (Hazzard, 1937, p. 329). These are mostly limestones which contain a fauna said to be of "very late Lower Triassic age." They may be equivalent to the *Tirolites* zone of the Virgin limestone member or to some higher part of the Moenkopi.

REGIONAL STRATIGRAPHY

The relationship of the Moenkopi formation to other Lower Triassic deposits of western America is as yet known only in a general way. An understanding of it hinges on the dating of various stratigraphic units, and these must be placed in a standard chronology in order to be compared.

Classification of the Lower Triassic faunas of America by J. P. Smith (1932, p. 15) recognizes five faunal zones. The lowest two—the *Otoceras* zone and the *Genodiscus* zone—are represented at Candelaria in west-central Nevada (Muller and Ferguson, 1939, p. 1584) and in Idaho, Montana, and Wyoming (Newell and Kummel, 1941, p. 205; 1942, p. 949). The *Meekoceras* or middle zone is present in many widely separated localities in California, Nevada, Idaho, Utah, Arizona, and Wyoming and doubtless marks the time of broadest seaways during the Lower Triassic epoch. Two upper zones, the *Tirolites* and *Columbites*, are represented in Idaho and northern Utah (Kummel, 1943, p. 322-323), and the *Tirolites* zone has recently been discovered in southern Utah also.

The *Meekoceras* and *Tirolites* zones are the only ones recognized in the Moenkopi formation. In southwestern Utah the *Meekoceras* fauna occurs in the Timpoweap or lowest member (Reeside and Bassler, 1922, p. 67; Newell and Kummel, 1942, p. 938), and it has been found as far east as Kaibab Gulch, 20 miles east of Kanab, Utah, in this member (Gregory, 1948, p. 227). In central Utah the *Meekoceras* fauna likewise occurs in the Moenkopi formation but is several hundred feet above the base, in the Sinbad limestone member. At this horizon it has been recorded from San Rafael Swell (Gilluly and Reeside, 1928, p. 66) and on the Green River farther east (McKnight, 1940, p. 58). The *Tirolites* fauna occurs in the Virgin limestone member in the St. George area, Utah, where it has been collected by Stanislaw Poborski (1953, p. 79).

The position of the *Meekoceras* fauna in various Lower Triassic sections beyond the recognized limits of the Moenkopi formation indicates their relationship to the Moenkopi. In the Confusion Range of central western Utah the fauna is at the base of the Lower Triassic (Bacon, 1948, p. 1045), as in the Moenkopi of southwestern Utah. In the central Wasatch, farther east (Scott, 1950, p. 1530), and in southeastern Idaho (Kummel, 1943, p. 319), it is at the base of the Thaynes formation and above the red beds of the Woodside—a situation similar to that at San Rafael Swell, Utah, where the *Meekoceras* fauna of the Moenkopi is in limestones underlain by several hundred feet of red beds.

Thus, if the *Meekoceras* zone as found in western America represents an approxi-

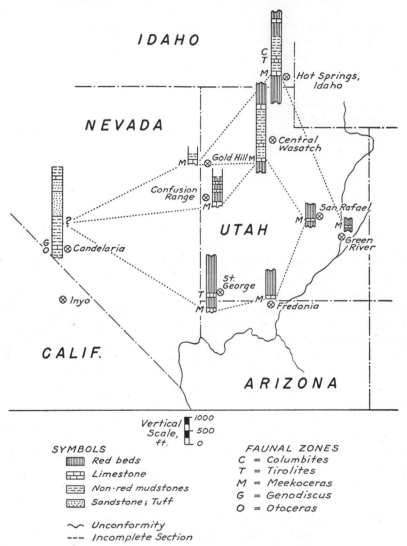

FIGURE 10.—*Columns of Lower Triassic strata in western America showing relative thicknesses and positions of strata with respect to ammonite zones*

Not shown are *Otoceras* and *Genodiscus* zones in Wyoming and Idaho.

mate time plane, the following conclusions are valid: (1) in southeastern California and western Nevada, and also in western Wyoming and southeastern Idaho, Lower Triassic marine sedimentation began far before the time represented by the *Meeko-ceras* fauna; (2) in central and east-central Utah red-bed deposition, probably continental, preceded accumulation of the *Meekoceras*-bearing limestones; and (3) in western and southwestern Utah sedimentation began with the accumulation of deposits containing the *Meekoceras* fauna.

The age of the thick Triassic deposits which lie above the *Meekoceras*-bearing beds in many localities is largely unknown. In southeastern Idaho and north-central Utah

these younger beds contain the zones of *Tirolites* and *Columbites* as well as unfossilif-
erous, higher strata of the Thaynes, and red beds of the Timothy (Kummel, 1943).
In the Uinta and Wasatch Mountains, Utah, red beds above the Thaynes limestone
are called the Ankareh (restricted) (Williams, 1945; Thomas and Krueger, 1946) and

TABLE 6.—*Nomenclature proposed for strata of central and northern Utah considered equivalent to Moenkopi*

After Stokes

Wasatch, W. Uintas (Williams, 1945)	Western Uintas (Thomas and Krueger, 1946)	Eastern Uintas (Thomas and Krueger, 1946)	Eastern Uintas (Williams, 1945)
Ankareh (restricted)	Ankareh (restricted)	....	....
Thaynes	Thaynes	....	Red Wash†
Woodside	Woodside	Woodside*	....

* Thaynes equivalents and restricted Ankareh believed to have been removed by pre-Upper
Triassic erosion
   † Undifferentiated Woodside and Ankareh restricted. Thaynes lost through pinch out

are undated (Table 6). Farther south Moenkopi beds of southwestern Utah, having
a corresponding position above the *Meekoceras* and *Tirolites* zones, likewise are of
uncertain age. Above the Virgin limestone member, where *Tirolites* occurs in this
area, are the middle red, Shnabkaib, and upper red members totaling more than
1000 feet thick and as yet not dated on the basis of fossils.

A possible approach for dating the upper units of the Moenkopi formation is
through critical analysis of the vertebrate fauna from the upper members of the
Moenkopi. These members are considered, on the basis of stratigraphic studies described in this paper, equivalent to the Moenkopi beds of the Little Colorado area
where S. P. Welles and associates have obtained extensive collections now being
prepared for study. Most of these specimens have not yet been examined sufficiently
to permit a statement concerning their age significance.

Vertebrate fossil material from one locality only in the Moenkopi formation has
been reported upon. This is at Holbrook, Arizona, where Welles (1947) obtained
from the uppermost or Holbrook member an assemblage of fish, amphibians, and
reptiles. He states that most of the specimens are of Lower Triassic type, but that
Cyclotosaurus, a distinctive and characteristic amphibian, is a Middle and Upper
Triassic form in Europe and South Africa. Thus, he concludes that, although available
evidence suggests an Early Triassic age for the Moenkopi, it may extend at least
into the Medial Triassic.

UNCONFORMITIES AND DIASTEMS
PRE-MOENKOPI UNCONFORMITY

Underlying the Moenkopi formation throughout the area of its distribution is a
major unconformity that marks the break between two eras. The hiatus involved

represents the time between forming of the Kaibab and equivalent formations of Leonard age (lower part of Permian) and deposition of *Meekoceras*-bearing beds in the Moenkopi formation (middle stage of Lower Triassic). In brief, it may be calculated in terms of some tens of millions of years.

Many geologists have noted the character of the erosion surface below the Moenkopi which extends over more than 80,000 square miles. In more than 30 papers features of this stratigraphic break as observed in various areas are described. Comprehensive discussions summarizing data and attempting to interpret the significance of the unconformity are presented by Dake (1920, p. 66–74), Longwell (1925, p. 93–106), and the writer (1938, p. 54–61).

Physical evidence that the pre-Moenkopi unconformity is widespread consists of irregular surfaces of erosion, of basal conglomerates, and, in some areas, of angular discordance. The magnitude of erosional channels, the character and extent of gravel deposits, and other features characteristic of the stratigraphic break vary greatly in different parts of the region, but nowhere do they appear indicative of important orogenic activity such as developed at the close of Permian deposition in many other parts of the world.

In southwestern Utah and southern Nevada pre-Moenkopi erosion has left its most conspicuous record of vigorous activity. In many localities relatively narrow canyons, cut into the Kaibab limestone, were filled with thick accumulations of boulders, pebbles, or rubble during either Early Triassic or pre-Triassic time. Local depressions, 50 to 100 feet deep, are cut into the Kaibab limestone of the Muddy Mountains area, Nevada (Longwell, 1921, p. 49), and a valley that cuts through the Kaibab and into the underlying Supai formation is reported in the Spring Mountains, Nevada (Glock, 1929, p. 333). Reeside (Personal communication, 1952) has pointed out, however, that the dating of such features is very uncertain, for the age of the conglomerate in the channels has never been conclusively determined, and some of the gravels appear to be of pre-Triassic age. He believes the buried valley, 700 feet wide and 250 deep, south of Hurricane, Utah, which he and Bassler described in 1922 (p. 60), is of Permian age.

Extensive and locally thick conglomerate deposits between the lowest fossil-bearing beds of the Moenkopi and the highest of the Kaibab formation in the southwestern Utah-southern Nevada region are described by several geologists. Lee (1907, p. 362) states that conglomeratic beds, 125 feet thick, make up the bottom of the Moenkopi formation near Cedar City, Utah. Longwell (1925, p. 105) describes a 65-foot, uninterrupted deposit of conglomerate, including some angular or subangular boulders up to 2 feet in diameter in the Spring Mountains, Nevada. Gregory and Williams (1947, p. 226) refer to varying amounts of conglomerate, the gravels of which were derived locally as shown by included fossils of Kaibab type, by angularity, and, in places, by large size. All of these gravels were referred to the Timpoweap member of the Moenkopi formation, but, as previously stated, Reeside (Personal communication, 1952) points out that some of the conglomerates clearly are of Permian age and that the Kaibab-Moenkopi boundary is not established for most parts of this area on fossil evidence.

Eastward from the area described, Moenkopi deposits likewise clearly illustrate that they were deposited on an ancient erosion surface, but here the topographic relief was far less. Exposures in Circle Cliffs, along the Fremont River, and in San Rafael Swell show few places where channelling or scouring is notable (McKee, 1938, p. 57).

Best evidence of unconformity in eastern Utah is where Permian strata representing different horizons underlie the basal Moenkopi of adjoining areas. In the San Rafael Swell "disappearance and reappearance of Kaibab limestone between Coconino sandstone and the Moenkopi formation" has been noted by Gilluly (1929, p. 81) and farther east by Baker (1946, p. 57). In the Fremont River area and at Circle Cliffs a comparison of sections in close proximity shows the presence or absence of "marker" beds in the Kaibab limestone that demonstrate removal locally of as much as 40 feet of limestone (Gregory and Moore, 1931, p. 45) and "probably two hundred feet or more" across the area (Dake, 1920, p. 65).

Near the northeastern limits of Moenkopi deposition, along the Colorado-Utah border, examples of Paleozoic strata that were folded and bevelled prior to Moenkopi deposition have been described from several localities. On the west side of the Colorado River near Moab, Utah, an angular discordance of 4° occurs between the Permian Cutler formation and the Moenkopi, and in the canyon below Moab both the Cutler and underlying Rico are cut out so that the Moenkopi rests on the Pennsylvanian Hermosa formation (Baker, 1933, p. 33). On the flank of the Cane Creek anticline southwest of Moab a slight angular discordance has been observed (McKnight, 1940, p. 61), and in Castle Valley to the northeast the unconformity systematically cuts through Cutler beds, reducing the formation to a very small thickness (Dane, 1935, p. 43).

In the Arizona region east and south of Grand Canyon the contact between the red Moenkopi formation and the underlying gray Kaibab limestone is conspicuous. The general flat, even surface developed during time of unconformity is especially noticeable and contrasts with the marked topographic relief at the same horizon farther west. Where small channels have been dissected in the otherwise flat surface of the resistant limestone, their sides are steplike or straight-walled. Here and there conglomerate beds, containing mostly small subangular gravels of chert, but locally composed of limestone pebbles, fill shallow depressions. In higher areas of the erosion surface red or yellow, shaly mudstones lie directly on the Permian limestone surface (McKee, 1938, p. 55).

Contrasting views regarding development of the pre-Moenkopi erosion surface have been entertained. The "smooth contact between the two formations (Cutler, Moenkopi) seems to indicate marine planation rather than subaerial channeling" according to Dane, (1935, p. 52). Elsewhere he states (p. 53) that the flat surface might be due to "coastal-plain peneplanation during Lower Triassic transgression, acting on a surface that probably was already reduced to moderate relief as a result of prolonged late Pennsylvanian and Permian erosion." He explains coarse debris that occurs throughout the Moenkopi of the area studied in eastern Utah by assuming a source of supply east of his postulated peneplane surface.

In contrast to the planation theories of Dane, resulting from studies in the northeastern part of the basin, Longwell (1925, p. 106) considers that the hill and valley topography and the channeling at the Triassic-Permian boundary in the western part of the region suggest widespread, rapid flooding of a surface developed through subaerial erosion. The deeper valleys clearly were formed through erosion of the land, and they appear to have been largely filled with locally derived gravels, including some of boulder size, before the first definite marine deposits (limestones) were laid down. Eastward, in northern Arizona and southern Utah, the basal as well as all later Moenkopi deposits are considered of continental origin; so here also it seems unlikely that marine planation was responsible for surface features exhibited at the unconformity.

Possibly both theories of origin apply to the erosion surface at the Triassic-Permian unconformity. In the northern part of the region the Moenkopi formation began to be deposited earlier than to the south as shown by the stratigraphic position of the *Meekoceras* zone. Likewise, deposition started earlier in southwestern Utah than in southeastern Utah or northern Arizona. Thus, marine or coastal-plain bevelling may have preceded early Moenkopi deposition in the north where initial deposits are considered marine (Gilluly and Reeside, 1928, p. 65), but may not have been a factor to the south where continental sedimentation began the sequence of Lower Triassic deposits.

INTRAFORMATIONAL BREAKS

Between the prominent, widespread unconformities that mark the base and the top of the Moenkopi formation, many local unconformities and diastems occur. With one probable exception, none appears to be of any considerable extent. They represent the type of local erosional feature that normally accompanies continental deposition where streams are fluctuating, depositional basins are silting up, and new basins are being formed.

An unconformity that appears to represent a major break is above the lower red member and below the Virgin limestone member. This break was first noted by Gregory (1952, p. 61), who has found evidence of it in many places throughout southwestern Utah. He lists several localities where ridge-and-valley topography developed on red mudstones has relief up to 10 or 15 feet in less than an acre, and he describes a southward and westward progressive bevelling of red beds in Kanab Valley with a resulting decrease in thickness of 100 feet in 3 miles. On the west face of Little Creek Mountain, north of the Arizona-Utah boundary, Gregory found the Virgin limestone member to vary from 8 feet to 81 feet in less than half a mile, with accompanying truncation of beds in the lower red member.

The significance of the unconformity between the lower red and Virgin limestone members is not known. Its magnitude may be sufficient to justify its recognition as a formational boundary, but further study will be necessary to determine this point. Recent work by Stanislaw Poborski (Personal communication, 1951) has shown that in the area west of St. George, Utah, the Virgin limestone rests on middle Kaibab limestone beds (*Dictyoclostus bassi* fauna) in one place and on late Kaibab limestone beds (*Bellerophon* fauna) in another, both less than 2 miles from a section containing the lower red and Timpoweap members between the Virgin limestone and the Kaibab. This suggests vigorous subaerial erosion after deposition of the lower red member and before an advance of the sea in which the Virgin limestone was formed. In brief, there appears to be a repetition of the events that inaugurated Moenkopi deposition in that area—*i. e.*, erosion, marine transgression, and basin silting by red sediments.

Unconformities at other horizons in the Moenkopi are locally prominent but appear to be of limited extent. One notable example, in the cliff face at Tan Seeps in San Rafael Swell, Utah, is recorded by Gilluly (Gilluly and Reeside, 1928, p. 65), and another covering several square miles in the Green River area is described by McKnight (1940, p. 54). Most conspicuous of such breaks are those between massive, cliff-forming sandstones or siltstones, which appear to represent stream deposits, and the red mudstones of flood-plain or tidal-flat deposits. Excellent examples of erosion surfaces on the massive beds occur along the Little Colorado Valley, Arizona, near Concho and near Wupatki.

Less prominent breaks or diastems are recognized in hundreds of localities where thin beds or lenses of mud pellets or of limestone pebbles occur in the sequence. These deposits are, for the most part, only inches thick, though some are 2 or more feet. They vary laterally from a few to many feet, and some of the limestone pebble beds extend for miles. Such intraformational conglomerates are composed of locally derived and poorly consolidated mud and clay pellets or rounded limestone pebbles that fill depressions or channels in other rock types. In some places they contain abundant bone fragments which show the results of rolling and wear. Their chief significance is that they emphasize the repeated break-up and redeposit of sediments under this type of continental environment.

POST-MOENKOPI UNCONFORMITY

An erosion surface of wide extent occurs between the Moenkopi formation and superjacent Upper Triassic deposits. The Shinarump conglomerate, which in most places is the overlying formation, contrasts greatly in color, hardness, and general character with the Moenkopi; so detailed features of the unconformity are readily detected. Virtually every geologist to have described these formations, except Ward (1901, p. 406) who believed the contact between them to be gradational, and Darton (1925, p. 119) who found "no evidence of any notable unconformity or time break," has recorded conspicuous examples of the erosion surface above the Moenkopi.

The Moenkopi-Shinarump contact is wavy and irregular even within short distances. Channels and pockets of various sizes, excavated in weak red mudstones and filled with gray Shinarump sandstone and conglomerate, are numerous. Equally common are hills or mounds of red Moenkopi that stick up into the Shinarump or even rise above it like islands (Fig. 11). In such places Chinle deposits rest upon beds of Moenkopi, and as these formations are similar in degree of hardness as well as in general appearance, the contact between them is difficult to locate.

The pre-Shinarump erosion surface locally is very conspicuous. A large Shinarump-filled channel in the Moenkopi near Paria, Utah, is illustrated by Walcott (1890. Fig. 12), and others near Pipe Springs, Utah, are shown by Davis (1903, p. 15, Fig. 5,) Residual mounds of Moenkopi surrounded by Shinarump conglomerate, located in the Little Colorado River area, are figured by Gregory (1914, Figs. 6, 7, 8). Additional typical illustrations of the contact are shown in this paper (Fig. 11). These and many others described from all parts of the region of Moenkopi distribution show plainly that the unconformity is the result of a long period of subaerial erosion, and not an intraformational feature.

The time represented by the hiatus involved in the Moenkopi-Shinarump unconformity is difficult to appraise. (1) The age of the topmost beds in the Moenkopi is

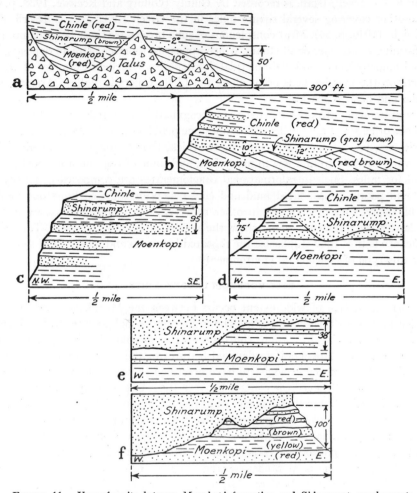

FIGURE 11.—*Unconformity between Moenkopi formation and Shinarump conglomerate*
(a) 11 miles north of Moab Bridge, Utah, (b) 1 mile west of Castle Creek, Moab, Utah, (c) (d) 9 miles southwest of Navajo Bridge, Arizona, (e) 6 miles south of Cameron, Arizona, (f) head of Soap Creek, 8.8 miles west of Navajo Bridge, Arizona.

not known. Deposition of the formation over much of its outcrop area began at or before the time of the *Meekoceras* fauna (middle zone of Lower Triassic), but sedimentation probably did not end until much later in the Early Triassic or even in the Medial Triassic, as suggested by certain of the vertebrate fauna in uppermost red beds and by comparison of its thickness with dated Triassic strata in Idaho. (2) The age of the overlying Shinarump conglomerate likewise is not known. Most geologists

(Baker, 1946, p. 61, and others) consider this formation merely a basal conglomerate of the thick Chinle formation. As the Chinle is known on fossil evidence to be of Late Triassic age, the Shinarump is considered probably to be the same. Furthermore, fossil plants in the Shinarump indicate Late Triassic age (Daugherty, 1941, p. 9). Stokes (1949, p. 79), on the other hand, believes this formation represents a type of pediment deposit, developed during a general period of erosion, and, therefore, he concludes that "its distribution and growth involved most of the Middle Triassic time."

During the period of Moenkopi-Shinarump hiatus, considerable crustal disturbance must have taken place in surrounding areas. The great volume of well-rounded gravels of durable rock types suggests uplift of surrounding regions sufficient to inaugurate swift erosion at the source and powerful transportation into the basin of deposition. This regional uplift must have taken place in central or southern Arizona (McKee, 1951, p. 494) and probably also in the Colorado region to the east.

Near the northeastern margin of the Moenkopi depositional basin some upwarping must have taken place during the pre-Shinarump hiatus (McKnight, 1940, p. 50). A renewal of movement along the general axis of the Moab anticline apparently was intense enough to raise the complete thickness of Moenkopi deposits above the base level of erosion as shown by angular discordance. East and southeast of this region in parts of Colorado and New Mexico, the Shinarump and Chinle formations overlap the easternmost Moenkopi and rest upon older rocks.

LITHOLOGY
THICK-BEDDED SANDSTONE AND SILTSTONE

CHARACTERISTICS: Under the heading of *thick-bedded sandstone and siltstone* of the Moenkopi formation are grouped those relatively coarse-grained detrital sedimentary rocks characterized by (1) massive, structureless beds, (2) thick beds cross-stratified on a medium to large scale, or (3) flat beds ranging in thickness from a few inches to several feet. Such deposits tend to be ledge forming or cliff forming because of their comparatively great resistance. They contrast with the slope-forming, shaly siltstones and also with the brittle or crumbly, structureless claystones and mud-stones that form the other two main types of detrital rock in the formation and that apparently represent different environments of deposition.

The results of mechanical analyses, examination of thin sections, and other textural studies indicate that rocks of this type are composed largely of detrital quartz grains that are angular to subangular and weakly to moderately well cemented, mostly with lime. Iron-oxide cement occurs in some specimens. Individual grains are principally of quartz, though orthoclase, chert, magnetite, muscovite, and apatite are also present. Most of these minerals are fairly durable, and the assemblage appears to be one that has been moderately reworked and sorted before deposition.

A series of mechanical analyses of samples from the *lower massive sandstone* along the Little Colorado Valley between Holbrook and Cameron (Black Point), Arizona, illustrates the character of this type of sediment (Table 7). All the samples analyzed show the dominant size grade to be in the *very fine sand* class (between $\frac{1}{16}$ and $\frac{1}{8}$ mm.), and most of them represent medium sorting according to the classification of

Payne (1942, p. 1707), for 90 per cent of each sample involves either three or four grade sizes. Some beds typical of this class are characterized by silt-sized quartz particles rather than by very fine sand, but other characteristics are similar.

TABLE 7.—*Mechanical-analysis determinations of lower massive sandstone samples*

Prepared by L. F. Brady

FROM SINKS TO GRAND FALLS

(In per cent)

	Grand Falls G1.2682	Leupp G1.2678	Meteor Crater G1.2692	Winslow G1.1962	Woodruff Butte G1.2246	Sinks G1.2363
Soluble in HCl...................	27.4	11.8	12.4	22.4	15.2	35.2
Medium sand.....................	....	8.2	.9	.....	.....	.....
Fine sand......................	4.9	15.4	24.7	14.4	6.8	21.6
Very fine sand..................	68.0	62.6	57.5	65.5	75.6	41.4
Pan...........................	26.9	13.6	16.9	20.1	17.7	37.0
	99.8	99.8	100.0	100.0	100.1	100.0

FROM CRACK-IN-THE-ROCK TO MOENKOPI WASH

(In per cent)

	Moenkopi Wash G1.1913	G1.1914	Poverty Tank G1.1925	West of Black Point G1.1977	G1.1979	G1.1980	East of Black Point G1.2029
Soluble in HCl...................	24.	15.2	24.	23.2	24.8	3.6	13.2
Medium sand.....................	23.7	1.4	.....	.....	.....	4.1	.....
Fine sand......................	25.	19.8	23.7	3.9	12.9	22.4	7.8
Very fine sand..................	37.5	63.7	56.6	60.7	43.5	62.7	81.1
Pan...........................	13.8	15.1	19.7	35.4	43.5	10.8	11.1
	100.0	100.0	100.0	100.0	99.9	100.0	100.0

Original structures common in the thick-bedded sandstone and siltstone include two principal types of cross-stratification, cusp ripple marks, impressions of plant stems, and casts of footprints. Some of the cross-stratification is of the shallow festoon type formed through channel scour and fill; some is of the truncated wedge variety indicating fluctuating directions of current. The abundant cusp ripple marks likewise indicate strong and variable current action. Small interference ("tadpole") ripple marks such as develop around bars or other obstacles are locally present (Fig. 17). Amphibian footprints, the casts of which occur in this sandstone, were formed in mud that was subsequently covered by sand. A majority of the amphibian (but not reptile) skeletal remains in the formation have been found in these sandstones.

DISTRIBUTION: The relative amount of thick-bedded sandstone and siltstone is greater in eastern Arizona or toward the source than in sections farther west, as might

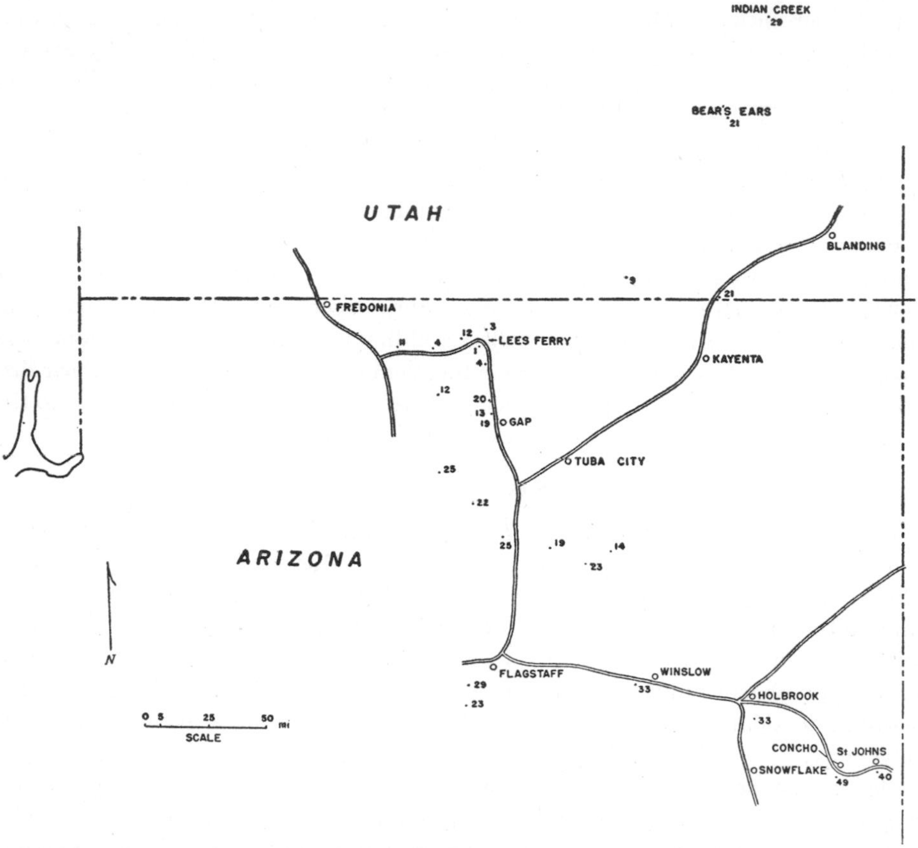

FIGURE 12.—*Per cent of total deposits represented by thick-bedded sandstones and siltstones in principal measured sections*

be expected. Percentages calculated for localities along the Little Colorado River, the Echo Cliffs, and a few places in southeastern Utah are shown in Figure 12. A second striking feature of distribution shown by this map is the very marked decrease in sand from the Little Colorado area northward to Lees Ferry. Possibly this also is explained as the result of distance from source, which suggests that at least two sources—one to the southeast (Zuni Mountain area) and the other to the northeast (Uncompahgre area)—were furnishing sediment to the Moenkopi deposits. More data of the same type from sections to the north and west of those indicated on the map are needed to establish fully the trends indicated.

Thick-bedded sandstones and siltstones are in both the lower (Wupatki) member and the upper (Holbrook) member, but not in the middle (Moqui) member of the

Little Colorado Valley. They include the "lower massive sandstone" near the formation base and various resistant sandstones that weather into forms referred to as "rock babies" in the upper part. All these sandstones are correlated with the upper members of the Moenkopi as found in southwestern Utah, however, and in that area sandstones appear to be restricted to the upper units. Thus, evidence suggests that introduction into the Moenkopi basin of thick-bedded sands and silts began, presumably, as a result of crustal uplifts in the source areas, and was followed by gradual westward advances of the sand blankets during at least two stages in Moenkopi history.

ORIGIN: Sedimentary structures within the thick-bedded sandstones and siltstones of the Moenkopi formation indicate their origin as fluviatile deposits and suggest an environment of deposition distinct from that in which other detrital sediments of the formation accumulated. The types of large-scale cross-stratification, the abundant and irregular cusp ripple marks, and the relatively coarse texture of the grains suggest constantly fluctuating current action of streams. Associated with these deposits in many places, furthermore, are mud pellets and limestone pebbles, derived from local break-up of deposits, and the worn bone fragments of vertebrate animals. Their distribution shows that these sands apparently were derived from an area or areas to the east and spread as wide sheets over relatively flat surfaces of deposition.

SHALY SILTSTONE

CHARACTERISTICS: The term *shaly siltstone* is applied to one of three types of detrital sediment that are quantitatively significant in the Moenkopi formation. Rocks included in this group characteristically split into thin layers, mostly between a quarter and half an inch in thickness. Some break with flat, even surfaces, but many others with ripple-marked tops or bottoms. In most places the shaly siltstone is weak reddish brown or pale reddish brown, but locally it is a yellowish brown, probably the result of deoxidation. Where associated with gypsum in certain members, it is a light olive gray.

Shaly siltstone of the Moenkopi is composed largely of silt-sized ($\frac{1}{16}$-$\frac{1}{256}$ mm.) angular fragments, chiefly of quartz, in a matrix of clay. Some is weakly cemented by iron oxide, calcium carbonate, or both. The amount of argillaceous matrix is variable so that siltstone grades into claystone, but a large majority of samples are definitely gritty to the feel as a result of high silt content. In resistance to weathering, it is intermediate between (1) the thick-bedded sandstone that forms ledges and cliffs and (2) the very crumbly, brittle, structureless claystone of the formation. Siltstone of this type characteristically forms slopes or benches.

Sedimentary structures are both varied and distinctive in the shaly siltstone deposits. By far the most abundant and conspicuous are parallel-type ripple marks, very numerous wherever the shaly silstone occurs. Probably their abundance in this formation is rivalled by few other deposits of the geologic column. Associated structures include shrinkage cracks, casts of salt cubes, reptile tracks, and worm borings.

DISTRIBUTION: Red shaly siltstone constitutes an appreciable part of the Moenkopi in almost all localities in which this formation is represented. Exceptions are in the thin deposits near the eastern margin of distribution (*e. g.*, St. Johns and Concho,

Arizona) where coarser detrital sediments form a high percentage of the deposits. Elsewhere within the area studied, shaly siltstone is distributed throughout all members of the formation, though the total amount varies considerably from place to place (Fig. 13). In sections along the Little Colorado River southeast of Cameron

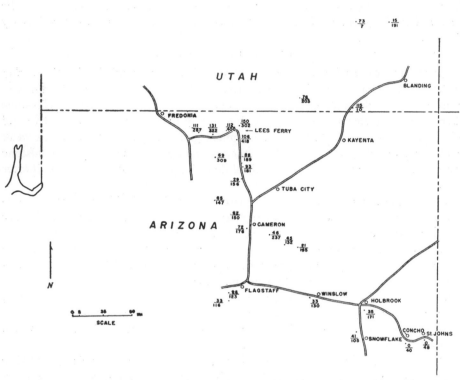

FIGURE 13.—*Thicknesses in feet of shaly siltstone (numerator) and structureless mudstone (denominator) in Moenkopi formation of northern Arizona and southern Utah*

this siltstone ranges from 20 to 50 feet thick, from Cameron north to Lees Ferry it is between 50 and 100 feet, and west of Lees Ferry between 100 and 150 feet.

Although in a majority of sections the shaly siltstone seems to constitute the major part of the red beds, detailed studies indicate (Fig. 13) that structureless mudstone has a total thickness about twice that of the siltstone in most places, and is four or five times as thick in some. The significance of this is that the mudstone represents sediments formed for the most part through settling in quiet waters, whereas the siltstone is a product of accumulation through current action.

ORIGIN: Evidence from textures and structures, indicating that the shaly siltstone of the Moenkopi formation is the result of mud-flat deposition, is abundant. Shrinkage cracks, casts of salt cubes, and reptile tracks show that at least periodically the area had a subaerial environment. On the other hand, the great abundance of parallel-type ripple marks, in many places covering the surfaces of successive layers of silt, indicates moving water.

Whether the mud flats were tidal or river flood plain is difficult to determine. Various features of the ripple marks, especially their constancy in direction over wide areas, seem to suggest a tidal-flat environment as described in the section on ripple marks, though the evidence is by no means conclusive. The rarity of plant remains in sediments that should make a good medium of preservation and the abundance of salt casts favor the concept of a tidal-flat deposition. Furthermore, the tracks of reptiles, common in other deposits of the formation, are rare in this shaly siltstone.

STRUCTURELESS MUDSTONE

CHARACTERISTICS: Detrital sediments of very fine grain, consisting largely of clay particles and devoid of bedding or lamination, form 50 per cent or more of most sections of the Moenkopi in northeastern Arizona. Rock of this type is largely claystone characterized by smooth, even texture, but locally it is slightly gritty due to small admixtures of silt particles. Iron-oxide pigment gives the rock a characteristic weak reddish-brown color, but, along many fractures and contact surfaces, the mudstone is light olive gray, apparently the result of deoxidation attributable to ground-water activity.

Because the mudstone is weak and brittle and without bedding structures, outcrops characteristically weather into angular, irregular blocks, and these continually break into smaller and smaller fragments until buried and protected by talus. Except locally, where capped by resistant sandstone or siltstone, the structureless mudstone forms slopes. On most of these, bedrock is concealed by thin layers of debris, and frequently, to sample the beds, trenches must be dug.

Examination of thin sections of typical structureless mudstone from near Cameron, Arizona, shows a few scattered angular grains of microcline and quartz, ranging between .024 and .04 mm. in diameter, in a matrix of clay minerals, most of which are partly obscured by iron-oxide pigment.

DISTRIBUTION: In northern Arizona and southern Utah structureless mudstone occurs at many horizions throughout the Moenkopi formation. Near the eastern margin of the formation it is least important both quantitatively and proportionately. In the vicinity of Lees Ferry and Navajo Bridge, Arizona (Fig. 13), it is thickest proportionately and in total amount. In that area it averages about 400 feet thick and constitutes three fourths or four fifths of the entire formation.

ORIGIN: Lack of structures, rather than structures of distinctive type, constitutes the principal evidence from which conclusions regarding genesis can be made. Absence of stratification appears to result from deposition without sorting into layers; it can scarcely be attributed to subsequent destruction by organisms because of a lack of their traces or of any relict beds. Thus, the clay was probably uniformly deposited with its particles having random orientation, owing to rapid settling in bodies of standing water. Whether these waters were fresh or marine is not known.

No original surface structures such as shrinkage cracks, ripple marks, or salt casts are preserved in the mudstone. Their absence probably is due to an environment of deposition that was not favorable to their development. If, however, they had formed, they would have been destroyed because of the manner in which this rock weathers. It breaks down into small blocks and chips, devoid of bedding surfaces. In some places, top surfaces of this mudstone once contained reptile tracks and shrinkage cracks, as shown by casts preserved on the under sides of covering sandstone or siltstone beds. This indicates withdrawal of waters before a particular mud deposit was buried by stream-borne sand.

MUD-PELLET CONGLOMERATE

Mud-pellet conglomerates are among the most distinctive types of deposit in the Moenkopi formation, although quantitatively they are negligible. These conglomerates form thin beds or lenses, ranging from 1 inch or less up to 1 or more feet thick, and they occur at many horizons throughout the entire area of Moenkopi distribution. Their chief significance is as a record of intraformational "breaks." Although individual deposits are very limited in extent, their recurrence in hundreds of places testifies to the vast number of pauses in sedimentation, accompanied by local erosion and development of mud pellets or mud balls.

Among the mud-pellet conglomerates many varieties are recognized. In most of them the pebbles or pellets are deep red-brown or greenish-gray clay. These pellets are irregular in shape, though a flattened ellipsoid is the most characteristic form. Others are spherical, giving rise to the name of "mud balls." In a large majority the corners and edges are subrounded, and diameters range between an eighth and half an inch. Exceptions are at the Bears Ears, Utah, in bed 6 where mud balls up to 8 inches in diameter occur (Pl. 4A), and 12 miles northwest of Cameron, in bed 19, where they are 3 inches across.

Nearly all the common rock types in the Moenkopi formation serve as matrix for mud pellets. In massive white or buff sandstone beds of stream-deposited type, local accumulations of deep-red or green pellets give conspicuous color contrast, and, where the soft clay balls have disintegrated and washed away, molds show prominently in the sandstone. Mud pellets likewise occur in thin-bedded siltstones and in limestones. Furthermore, in a few places they are associated with limestone pebbles and in others mixed with granules of chert or similar durable rock derived from the underlying Kaibab formation. The skull of a capitosaurid amphibian, preserved in a matrix of mud pellets, is figured by Peabody (1948, Pl. 24A).

Mud pellets and mud balls in the Moenkopi appear to have developed through weathering and break-up of clay deposits, small particles of which are washed about locally or transported short distances. The soft, weak character of the material indicates that the pellets could not have endured long transportation. The degree of rounding on nearly all specimens shows that the material was unconsolidated at the time of development. Where the lithified equivalent of this clay, as represented by various beds of the Moenkopi, is affected by erosion, it does not become rounded but crumbles into progressively smaller angular particles.

LIMESTONE GRAVEL CONGLOMERATE

Limestone gravel conglomerate is a type of intraformational deposit not uncommon in some parts of the Moenkopi formation. Characteristics of typical examples are presented in Table 8. In certain places this conglomerate occurs as lenses only a few

TABLE 8.—*Characteristics of limestone gravel conglomerates in northeastern Arizona and central eastern Utah sections*

Locality	*Bed*	*Thickness*	*Matrix*	*Max. gravel (Inches)*	*Av. gravel (Inches)*	*Gravel composition*	*Associated features*
St. Johns	3	Lense	Lime	½	......	Limestone	....
Concho	5	4½ feet	Calcareous silt	½	¼	2 types limestone	Amphibian skulls and interclavicles
Concho	9	Top zone, 30-foot bed	Fine sand	......	¼	....	....
Woodruff	4	½ foot	Silty lime	½	¼	2 types limestone	....
Woodruff	6	2½ feet	Silty lime	½	¼	Limestone	....
Winslow	5	½ foot	Fine sand	¼	......	Limestone	....
Winslow	7	7½ feet	Fine sand	......	......	Limestone	....
Winslow	12	Lense	....	......	......	Limestone	Bone fragments
Meteor Crater	4	Top of 1-foot bed	Lime	......	......	Limestone clay pellet	....
Wupatki	8	Top 2-inch zone, sandstone bed	Lime	......	......	Limestone clay pellet	....
Black Falls	4	½ foot	Calcareous silt	½	¼	Limestone	Tooth, plant stems
W. Black Pt.	8	Lense in sandstone	Calcareous silt	......	¼	Limestone	Bone fragments, plant stems
S. Cameron	7	Base of 2½-foot limestone bed	....	¼	⅛	Limestone	Bones, plants
White Canyon	10	1½–6 feet	Siltstone	½	¼	Limestone	....

feet across, but elsewhere it extends as thin layers for several miles, making excellent marker beds. Because it contains many worn skeletal fragments of amphibians, reptiles, and fish, it sometimes is referred to as "bone conglomerate." It is characteristically light olive gray.

The limestone gravels in this conglomerate are mostly of granule size, though a few have diameters ranging up to an inch or more. Lithologic character and field relationships indicate derivation through the break-up of earlier deposits within the formation. Some appear to have been developed in place, possibly by wave or current action, for they are in a matrix of similar limestone. Others probably were transported short distances, for they include gravels representing two or three varieties of limestone. Furthermore, in some deposits the matrix is of silt or sand, and the associated beds above or below are stream-deposited sandstones.

Limestone gravels are associated in some deposits with mud pellets as might be expected, for both represent the products of intraformational erosion. Plant stems and water-worn bones of vertebrate animals in the conglomerate suggest an environment favorable for the accumulation and preservation of materials introduced by streams from surrounding areas. In the Valley of Fire, Nevada, one bed high in the section contains fresh-water (?) mollusk shells of a single species closely packed in among limestone pebbles of three types.

From a geographical standpoint most of the limestone gravel beds appear to be distributed on the landward margins of the depositional basin. They are especially numerous along the Little Colorado River area in northeastern Arizona and also in sections of central eastern Utah—both eastward-extending embayments of the basin. Sandstones of fluviatile origin also are relatively more numerous in these areas than elsewhere. In contrast, the thick Moenkopi sections of southwestern Utah, which are in part marine, contain relatively few of these conglomerates. Even farther east, near Lees Ferry, Arizona, where the Moenkopi is almost entirely mudstone with little sandstone, the limestone gravel conglomerates are rare or absent. Thus, there seems to be a relationship between this type of conglomerate and the shallow ponds or lakes and streams of marginal parts of the basin.

GYPSUM

DISTRIBUTION: In the Moenkopi formation, throughout much of the area of distribution, gypsum is a common constituent. It occurs as beds (Pl. 3A), lenses, and layers of concretions that apparently are primary deposits, and as crosscutting veins and seams (Pl. 3C) that clearly are secondary. Gypsum forming a cement occurs in shaly siltstones. It may be either primary or secondary, but most of it probably was precipitated when the silt was deposited.

Where the Moenkopi formation attains its maximum thickness in southwestern Utah, gypsum deposits are most extensive and prominent. Some gypsum is in each of the three red-bed members, occurring both as thin beds and as crosscutting veins, but it is most abundant in the Shnabkaib member (Pl. 2A, B). Here it forms beds, ranging from a few inches to 5 or more feet thick, that are associated with olive-gray, gypsiferous, shaly mudstones and claystones. The bedded gypsum is mostly massive but locally shows cross-stratification (Pl. 3B). It is fine-grained and ranges from pure white to pale green and pink. In general, beds are even and regular, although in places they fill channels in underlying units. Many extend for as much as a mile (Gregory, 1952, p. 61).

In southern Nevada where the Moenkopi formation is also thick (1500–2000 feet), gypsum constitutes an important part of the section. Detailed studies have not been made of the formation in this area, but Longwell (1928, p. 46–52) shows in measured sections that most of it is interbedded with "yellowish gray calcareous shale." The writer has observed that members of the Moenkopi formation recognized throughout southwestern Utah are also conspicuous in the Nevada sections and that the Shnab-kaib member is the one that contains most of the bedded gypsum. Longwell reports a lessening of limestone units with an increase in mudstone and gypsum toward the south and east in this area.

In eastern Utah and northeastern Arizona primary gypsum of the Moenkopi formation is relatively uncommon and occurs largely in thin beds or lenses. Secondary gypsum veins and seams, on the other hand, appear to be abundant in nearly all parts of the area.

Little Colorado Valley sections between Holbrook and Cameron, Arizona, contain bedded gypsum almost exclusively in the middle or Moqui member where it is associated with gray siltstones and claystones that contrast with red beds of the members above and below. The area to the north, from Cameron to Lees Ferry, examined by the writer (this paper), the Kaiparowits region of Utah studied by Gregory and Moore (1931, p. 48), the Moab district reported by Baker and others (1933, p. 34), and the Monument Valley area, Utah, examined by Baker (1936, p. 41) all contain few bedded gypsum deposits, and those that are recorded are thin or nodular. As in other areas, however, secondary gypsum veins are in various parts of most sections.

Still farther north, in the San Rafael Swell (Gilluly and Reeside, 1928, p. 65) and Salt Valley anticline (Dane, 1935, p. 44) of Utah, some moderately extensive beds of gypsum occur in the lower part of the formation. One gypsum bed in the Salt Valley anticline exceeds 6 feet in thickness (Dane, 1935, p. 44). In several localities gypsum rests unconformably on the underlying Cutler formation. Sections in this area are thicker than immediately southward (Fig. 7), and limestone units containing marine fossils suggest that the eastern margin of the sea extended farther eastward here than in the area to the south.

In summary, the following points seem to be significant:

(1) The gypsum beds are associated only with fine-grained sediments such as claystones and siltstones.

(2) The detrital sediments enclosing most of the larger gypsum deposits are light-colored (gray, yellow, white); comparatively few are red beds[2].

(3) Individual gypsum deposits range from a few inches to a few feet thick, and some of them are widespread, extending for more than a mile.

(4) Where the formation extends farthest eastward, in east-central Utah and in east-central Arizona, gypsum beds also extend eastward; in the area between, centered about the Arizona-Utah line, gypsum beds are almost absent.

---

[2] S. Poborski (Personal communication) reports gypsum in middle red member of the St. George, Utah, area, associated with reddish-brown siltstones. Other exceptions have been noted.

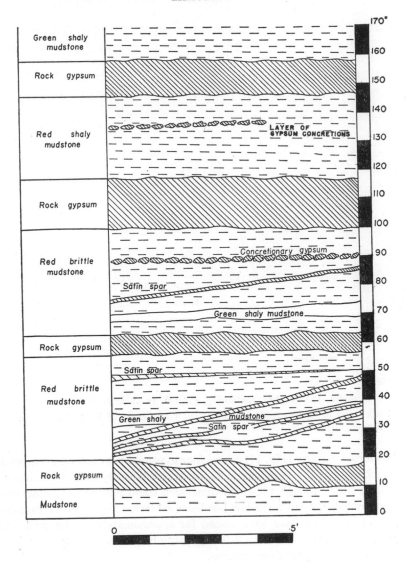

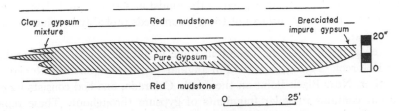

FIGURE 14.—*Section of gypsum deposits in Moqui member of Moenkopi formation 6 miles west of Holbrook, Arizona*

Lower drawing shows detail of gypsum bed in section above, showing extent and form.

CHARACTERISTICS OF GYPSUM: Detailed examination of gypsum beds and enclosing strata (Figs. 14, 15) reveals that all the deposits studied contained rock gypsum in layers or lenses 4 to 17 inches thick, alternated with fissile claystone or siltstone beds two to six times that thickness. Some gypsum beds farther west in the St. George area are reported to be much thicker (Poborski, Personal communication).

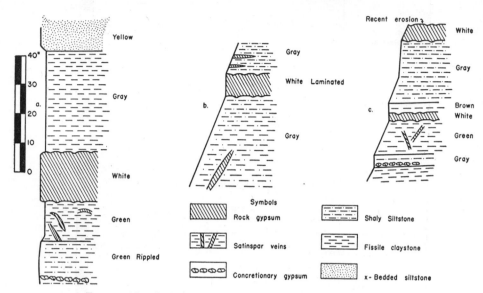

FIGURE 15.—*Sections containing gypsum in Shnabkaib member*
(a) 14.5 miles west of Navajo Bridge, Arizona; (b) 1 mile north of Fredonia, Arizona; (c) east side, Kaibab Gulch, Utah.

In the Holbrook locality (Fig. 14) one of four gypsum beds exposed averages about 2 feet in thickness and 25 feet in length. It was traced laterally to where it fingers into red mudstone, and, although the third dimension could not be fully observed, the deposit appears to represent a shallow bowl-shaped lens. Other deposits examined in the Little Colorado area have been traced for approximately a mile, and Gregory (Personal communication) records a 4-foot gypsum bed in southwestern Utah that is visible for several miles along the outcrop.

In all the bedded gypsum deposits studied in detail, irregularities along the bottom and top surfaces are present. Inasmuch as the mudstones above and below are evenly bedded, most of the wavy surfaces of the gypsum beds probably are due to swelling from hydration.

Brecciated gypsum beds are present in some localities. The eastern margin of a lens near Holbrook (Fig. 14) is formed of angular gypsum fragments with clay filling the interstices. Near Black Point on the Little Colorado, one bed consists largely of siltstone but contains irregular fragments of gypsum throughout. These represent extremes in the proportions of gypsum fragments to detrital sediments. No certain evidence is available to indicate whether such breccia beds are of the collapse type, related to hydration, or are the result of intraformational break-up.

Gypsum in some beds is relatively pure, structureless, and compact; in others it contains considerable admixtures of clay or silt, and in still others it contains thin partings of detrital sediments. A series of samples from a lens near Holbrook, Arizona, shows the following proportions of clay and silt:

	Per cent detritals
(1) Brecciated gypsum	3.1
(2) Massive white gypsum	1.5
(3) Concretionary gypsum	3.2
(4) Concretionary gypsum	4.0
(5) Massive brown gypsum	2.0

Although most gypsum beds examined in detail proved to be structureless, one near Fredonia, Arizona, showed a crude lamination consisting of thin, irregular layers of pure gypsum alternating with others of muddy gypsum. At a locality on the Vermilion Cliffs, 13 miles west of Navajo Bridge, a 13-foot bed of gypsum shows cross-stratification on a large scale with compound structure suggesting aeolian deposition (Pl. 3B). It seems likely that this thick bed, which is in the Shnabkaib member, may have been formed by the wind much as the white sands of Alamogordo, New Mexico, are being developed today.

ORIGIN OF GYPSUM: Gypsum is interbedded with fine detrital sediments in the Moenkopi of western Utah and southern Nevada and, less conspicuously, farther east. Such repetitions of a cycle suggest alternations of environmental conditions. Each sequence appears to represent mud deposition in a wide, shallow lagoon followed by a clearing of the waters during which evaporation and concentration brought about chemical precipitation.

In few, if any, parts of the area examined is the sequence of deposits that which should be expected from evaporation of normal sea water (Clarke, 1924, p. 219–221). Aphanitic limestone, developed through chemical precipitation at an early stage of concentration, does not underlie the calcium sulfate of higher concentration. Where limestone beds are present, they show no apparent relation to the gypsum.

The absence of a limestone bed underlying each gypsum deposit in the Moenkopi formation may be explained in either of two ways: (1) Normal sea water, before entering the particular ponds or lagoons where the gypsum was formed, may have had all calcium carbonate salts precipitated out in some other basin nearer the sea as postulated in the basin hypothesis of Branson (1915, p. 231–242). Thus calcium carbonate was not available in solution, and the first evaporites formed would necessarily be calcium sulfate. (2) The gypsum was not formed from sea water but from lakes fed by streams deficient in calcium carbonate. In this situation, like the first, calcium sulfate might be deposited without being preceded by the limestone.

Field evidence suggests that all the evaporite deposits of the Moenkopi formation were formed from the evaporation of waters originally marine. Favoring this hypothesis is (1) a decrease in thickness and amount of evaporites away from the areas marginal to marine deposits, and (2) the normal association of gypsum beds throughout the area with ripple-marked, shaly siltstones believed to be of tidal-flat origin, on the basis of independent evidence.

Possibly of considerable significance in interpreting the environment of gypsum deposition in the Moenkopi is the light coloring of associated detrital sediments in many places, in contrast to the extensive red beds elsewhere in the formation. This is especially well illustrated by the Shnabkaib member in the western Utah area and the Moqui member along the Little Colorado. These contain far more gypsum deposits than do any other units in the formation and, in both, the detrital deposits are largely gray, olive or yellow—not red.

Explanation of the light colors prevalent among the shaly siltstones associated with gypsum deposits, in contrast to the red-brown colors of similar shaly siltstones elsewhere in the formation, is sought in the environment of deposition. Clearly the incidence of oxidation is great on tidal flats because of intermittent subaerial exposure. The restricted areas of gypsum accumulation, however, were presumably covered by shallow water continuously during the time of precipitation and for considerable periods before and after. Iron normally is reduced on the sea floor, and, as pointed out by Zo Bell (1946, p. 478), burial in a reducing environment, in company with dissolved salts, causes mineralogical changes in mud. Conditions of restricted circulation are likely to cause an even more strongly reducing environment than in normal marine waters.

The nature of the basins in which gypsum accumulated is suggested by the form of the evaporite deposits. The lagoons or lakes must have ranged from a few feet to more than a mile in diameter. The thickness of deposits and their relations to enclosing shaly siltstones indicate that they were shallow depressions on a generally flat surface that sloped westward toward the sea. The thin beds in these deposits presumably constitute good time-rock datum planes.

LIMESTONE

DISTRIBUTION: The distribution of limestone beds within the Moenkopi formation appears to be significant in an interpretation of paleogeography. Where the formation attains a maximum thickness of 1500 to 2000 feet in southwestern Utah, not only are limestone deposits thickest, but also they form a relatively much greater proportion of the formation than elsewhere. On the other hand, where the sections of Moenkopi are thinnest, along the eastern borders of Utah and Arizona, there are no limestone deposits. Between these two extremes are areas with limestone intermediate in amount and proportion.

Because of insufficient data from certain areas, it is not yet possible to make a clastic ratio map[3] for the Moenkopi formation. Rough estimates, based on data from measured sections, indicate, however, that chemical deposits (limestone, dolomite, gypsum) together constitute between one-sixth and one-fourth of the formation in southwestern Utah. Farther east along Echo Cliffs and the lower part of the Little Colorado Valley in Arizona, they form one-twentieth to one-fiftieth or less of the total and are absent in the region of Monument Valley and the upper Little Colorado Valley.

In the thick deposits of southwestern Utah, limestones are best developed in the Timpoweap or basal member and in the Virgin member, several hundred feet higher, which likewise rests upon an unconformity. Thus, these limestones appear to repre-

---

[3] A map in which contour lines are developed around figures derived from ratio of chemical to detrital sediments.

sent deposits of transgression formed under waters that advanced from the geosyncline in Nevada, whereas the red beds above each limestone series are continental deposits that caused regression as their detritus forced the sea margins westward. In each of the red-bed members (Gregory, 1952, p. 60), some limestones occur, but they are, in general, thin and impure and apparently represent a transition from chemical to detrital deposition. They are reported most common in the lowest and highest parts of the members and lacking in the middle. No limestones have been noted by the writer in the lower red member.

Throughout the Moenkopi formation, limestone deposits are notably irregular, lenticular, and lensing. This feature is especially conspicuous in eastern Arizona sections where limestone beds that are prominent features of one section are absent in another not far away. Similar characteristics appear among limestone deposits of southwestern Utah, for Gregory (1952, p. 60, 61) refers to "sporadic lenses" and to "beds that retain thickness, composition, and texture for only short distances." Detailed studies have not been made of these strata, however; to what extent such generalizations apply to the more massive, thicker-bedded, fossiliferous limestones of the Timpoweap and Virgin members is not known. These limestone members as units are persistent features over a very wide area, but the individual beds within them may be more local and lensing than most limestones.

LITHOLOGIC CHARACTER AND ORIGIN: Limestones of the Moenkopi formation are of several distinct types representing different environments. Varieties of intermediate character are also present, however, suggesting complete gradation from one type to another as a result of several sedimentary processes working simultaneously. Mixed varieties include limestones with high content of angular rock fragments or gravels, those mixed with silt, and those with clay. Also represented are rocks containing various amounts of magnesium, some being classed as dolomite, others as dolomitic limestone, magnesian limestone, or calcitic limestone, according to the classification of Pettijohn (1950, p. 313).

Much of the limestone in the Moenkopi formation is dense, aphanitic, and thin-bedded. Other less common types are the oölitic, the dense, nodular, and the fine-grained fossiliferous. Some limestones are nearly white, but most are various shades of gray on fresh surface; this color apparently results largely from admixtures of clay, silt, and other detrital materials. In southwestern Utah some limestone beds are cross-stratified—the structures etching out prominently on weathered surfaces.

The local, lensing character of deposits, the evenness of grain, the lack of organic structures, and the thinness of bedding suggest that much of the limestone was formed as chemical precipitates through evaporation and concentration of fresh or sea water. Those deposits that form thin sheets or fill pockets among red beds must be of this type, for most of them appear to have formed in depressions isolated from the sea. The origin of certain other limestones such as those containing pelcypods or brachiopods in the marine beds of the Timpoweap and Virgin members is less easy to determine. Many of these might also represent chemical precipitates, insofar as the texture and structure give evidence, yet the possibility that organisms may have been responsible for their accumulation must also be entertained.

Petrographic studies of selected typical limestone samples from the Little Colorado

Valley area show large quantities of fine detrital quartz scattered through the carbonates. In some specimens calcite forms a crystalline mosaic, apparently the result of direct precipitation, but in others calcite grains show evidence of rounding and are interpreted as reworked or clastic sediment. A crude layering, due to successive zones

TABLE 9.—*Chemical analyses of Moenkopi limestones*

Analyses 1–4 by Hawley and Hawley, Douglas, Arizona; Analyses 5–11 by F. G. Hawley, Tucson, Arizona

Locality and horizon	SiO_2	Al_2O_3	Fe_2O_3	CaO	MgO
1. Meteor Crater, bed 4, amphibian horizon....	47.5	6.9	1.42	22.63	0.14
2. W. of Cameron Jct., 4.8 mi., bed 7, fossils...	53.8	7.5	2.21	18.31	0.36
3. W. of Winslow, bed 14, amphibian horizon..	56.7	8.0	2.14	13.55	0.79
4. W. of Winslow, bed 17, amphibian horizon..	59.0	5.8	2.64	13.45	1.58
5. Gap, 5 mi. north, bed 9, x-lam., thin........	43.0	7.35	1.7	21.22	2.32
6. Cedar Ridge, 10 mi. n., bed 16, rippled.....	46.4	6.68	1.2	20.45	2.46
7. Fredonia, 10 mi. s., bed 41, silty..........	38.8	7.35	1.5	15.46	7.86
8. Fredonia, 10 mi. s., bed 41, Virgin ls........	7.6	1.84	0.6	31.04	15.37
9. Fredonia, 10 mi. s., bed 47, mollusks........	10.6	2.82	0.6	28.50	14.20
10. Muddy Mtns., Nev., Virgin ls...........	4.0	1.43	0.57	51.40	1.70
11. Muddy Mtns., Nev., lower Virgin ls......	3.9	1.24	0.36	52.5	0.80
12. Muddy Mtns., Nev., lower Virgin ls......	44.0	6.42	0.79	26.3	1.30
13. Muddy Mtns., Nev., lower Virgin ls......	18.0	3.01	0.79	41.2	2.00
14. Frenchman Mtns., Nev., below Virgin ls..	8.2	0.96	1.14	27.8	18.50
15. Frenchman Mtns., Nev., below Virgin ls..	4.1	1.07	0.43	29.8	18.20

of great and little concentration of detrital particles, is apparent in some of the limestones.

Chemical analyses of 15 specimens (Table 9) support conclusions presented above concerning the genesis of rock types. Numbers 1 through 7 are all notably high in SiO_2 and Al_2O_3, apparently because of admixtures of detrital quartz and clay materials. These are the gray silty and clayey limestones that occur largely as isolated lenses among the red beds and that in a number of places have preserved the skeletal remains of vertebrate animals. They grade imperceptibly into calcareous siltstones and claystones. A typical sample from near Fredonia contains 40 per cent insoluble material, including 1 per cent fine sand, 13.5 per cent very fine sand, and 25.5 per cent silt and clay.

Analyses 8–13 (Table 9) illustrate marine limestones, typical of the Moenkopi type, some of which contain mollusks. With one exception the amount of detrital matter is small, and, in most, the MgO content is low. In contrast, specimens 14–15 have a notably high MgO content and are essentially dolomite. These specimens are from what probably are nonmarine deposits interbedded with red mudstones, and they may have formed in the concentrated waters of residual pools.

Certain limestones in the Timpoweap or basal member of the formation furnish evidence of clastic origin. At Kaibab Gulch, Utah, one bed of yellow to pink limestone, 22 feet thick, is cross-stratified on a large scale throughout and contains abundant casts of pelecypods. Other limestone beds near the base of the formation at this locality are flat-lying but contain coarse grains of quartz and angular fragments of chert and limestone, up to 4 inches in diameter. These indicate strong current action at the time the limestones formed.

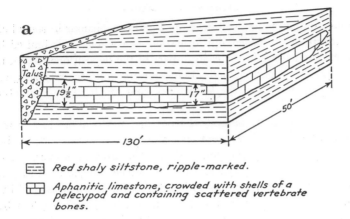

☷ Red shaly siltstone, ripple-marked.

⊞ Aphanitic limestone, crowded with shells of a pelecypod and containing scattered vertebrate bones.

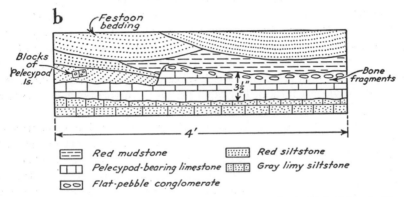

☰ Red mudstone   ▦ Red siltstone

⊞ Pelecypod-bearing limestone   ▤ Gray limy siltstone

⊙ Flat-pebble conglomerate

FIGURE 16.—*Typical examples of fresh-water (?) limestone deposits in Little Colorado River Valley* (a) 4.8 miles west of Cameron; (b) west of Black Point.

In the Virgin member of southwestern Utah evidence of shallow-water deposition and of reworked sediments likewise is demonstrated in many places. The lower part of the second limestone unit above the base is conspicuously cross-stratified locally, and the upper 3 feet of this unit is a crinoidal limestone composed largely of broken stem fragments (Poborski, Personal communication). Also in this area some of the limestone beds contain shrinkage cracks (Pl. 4C), indicating a temporary subaerial environment.

The presence of fresh-water (?) mollusks in clayey limestones has been noted in a few localities near the Little Colorado Valley, which is far eastward of the nearest definite marine deposits. These fossils are very poorly preserved pelecypods of a single undetermined genus, and locally they are concentrated almost sufficiently to form a coquina. Elsewhere the limestone contains few pelecypods but some fish fragments and amphibian bones. The sheetlike, localized character of these deposits is illustrated in Figure 16.

ORIGINAL STRUCTURES

CROSS-STRATIFICATION

Cross-stratification, although well developed and conspicuous in some beds, is not a prominent feature of the Moenkopi formation as a whole. It is limited largely to the thick-bedded sandstones in the eastern part of the depositional basin, to certain siltstones, and to a few limestone beds. It includes medium-scale types (planes 1–20 feet) expecially characteristic of the sandstones, and much ripple-lamination in the thin-bedded siltstones.

Many thick units of sandstone and siltstone in the Moenkopi locally weather to massive, nonstratified cliffs. They develop into rounded, so-called "rock babies" or into sheer, structureless walls. The same beds in other areas, however, show the patterns of large- to medium-scale cross-stratification etched out on their surfaces. Some of these structures are "planar cross-stratification" (Pl. 5B) as classified by McKee and Weir (1953, p. 385), and some are of the shallow trough variety (Pl. 5C). In most of the latter type examined, layers of sediment filling the channels show asymmetrical deposition—i.e., concentration from one side rather than even filling.

Medium-scale cross-stratification in sandstones and siltstones of the Moenkopi is interpreted as indicating stream deposition. The planar types probably represent sloping surfaces on the fronts of converging delta lobes. The shallow trough types are believed to result from channels carved by actively eroding streams and subsequently filled with sediment when changing water level caused deposition. This interpretation is in accord with evidence furnished by other primary structures such as the abundant cusp ripple marks and by associated fossils.

Ripple-lamination is abundant in the red shaly siltstones, but in relatively few places is it conspicuously etched by weathering to form a prominent feature of ledge faces (Pl. 8D). As should be expected from the tremendously great number and the variety of parallel ripple marks throughout the formation, the resulting lamination patterns include all the principal types such as those of (1) uniform deposition, (2) lee-side concentration, and (3) superposition out of rhythm, described by McKee (1939, p. 72). In some places pseudo-bedding planes, developed through successive ripple laminae forming with lee-side concentration, are prominent and look like true beds dipping with parallel planes (Pl. 6E).

Cross-stratification in limestone is conspicuous locally in the Timpoweap and the Virgin members where weathering etches the structures on exposed bedding surfaces. This cross-stratification is largely of the simple type, built forward on one plane, and of medium scale. One bed in the Virgin member, up to 5 feet in thickness, is marked by these structures for at least 10 miles in one direction, according to Stanislaw Poborski (Personal communication, 1951). Thus, large deposits of limestone in the Moenkopi clearly are of clastic origin.

GNARLY OR CONTORTED BEDDING

In the Moenkopi, as in many formations of continental origin, gnarly or contorted bedding is not uncommon. Most of that noted in the Moenkopi involves sandstone beds 6 inches to 2 feet thick that seemingly have been warped or twisted. No detailed studies have been made of these deposits or their origin, but they clearly developed as penecontemporaneous features of deposition. The irregular, blurred margins of folded beds and the fading out of structures away from a center of movement indicate that the sand was saturated or nearly saturated when either slumping or compression from overloading affected it.

Other examples of structures developed in unconsolidated sediments are small-scale folds in fine-grained detrital rocks and in limestones. Crumpled shaly beds between horizontal strata of sandstone are recorded by Frank Peabody (Personal communication, 1951). Illustrations of laminated beds of limestone in the Virgin member, west of St. George, Utah, folded locally, then beveled, before the next flat-lying strata were formed on top (Pl. 10B), have been observed by the writer. Contorted bedding structures, attributed to subaqueous flowage and subsequent truncation of folded beds in micaceous sandstones, are recorded by Dane (1935, p. 46) from eastern Utah.

RIPPLE MARKS

Ripple marks, by far the most common and characteristic structure of the Moenkopi formation, are abundant in all the red-bed members and in the Shnabkaib, and are found throughout the region of Moenkopi outcrop. Virtually every geologist who has described the formation has referred to them, and many have mentioned their significance as indicators of a shallow-water environment.

An attempt has been made by the writer to analyze and classify ripple marks of the Moenkopi and to obtain quantitative data on size and distribution. Three hundred specimens have been examined, and, for each, data were obtained on: (1) the type of ripple, (2) the direction of movement (3) the height of the crests, (4) the distance between crests, (5) the ripple index, (6) the length of parallel troughs, (7) the number of crests in series, and (8) associated sedimentary features.

Two main types of ripple mark, both the result of water-current action, are very common in the Moenkopi, and a third, developed through wave action, is represented in a few areas. Numerous subtypes or variations of these ripple forms also are recognized. Distribution of the main types very definitely indicates a relationship to lithology, suggesting that each was formed in response to a particular process of sedimentation.

Of the two basic types of asymmetrical ripple marks, the more common one is characterized by even, parallel ridges and troughs, averaging about 1 inch from crest to crest. It is largely confined to the surfaces of thin, shaly siltstones believed to have been developed on extensive mud flats, either tidal or flood plain. The second principal variety is much larger and more irregular, normally appearing as a series of cusps or crescentic mounds and hollows. It occurs mostly among thick-bedded siltstones and sandstones that apparently formed under the stronger and more diverging current action of active stream channels. No ripple marks are present, so far as known, among the brittle mudstones, doubtless because they developed through settling of mud particles in quiet water.

RIPPLE MARKS CHARACTERISTIC OF MUDFLAT DEPOSITS: The name *parallel ripple mark* is used here to designate the common current variety found on shaly siltstones.

This type is extremely numerous at many horizons and in every area of Moenkopi outcrop. It covers large surfaces of rock, apparently extending without interruption for many tens of feet in some places. West of Cameron, Arizona, one set of 880 successive crests spans a distance of 110 feet. Many of the parallel ripples are very uniform,

TABLE 10.—*Indices of ripple marks, parallel type, Moenkopi formation*

Index	5	6	7	8	9	10	11	12	13	14	15
Per cent (300 readings)	5	9	7	18	12	9	15	8	5	4	8

TABLE 11.—*Amplitude of ripple marks, parallel type, Moenkopi formation*

Inches	$\frac{1}{32}$	$\frac{1}{16}$	$\frac{3}{32}$	$\frac{1}{8}$	$\frac{5}{32}$	$\frac{3}{16}$	$\frac{7}{32}$	$\frac{1}{4}$	$\frac{9}{32}$	$\frac{5}{16}$	$\frac{11}{32}$	$\frac{3}{8}$
Per cent (300 readings)	2	15	20	34	7	13	0	6	0	1	0	2

TABLE 12.—*Length, crest to crest, of ripple marks, parallel type, Moenkopi formation*

Inches	0–.5	.5–1	1–1.5	1.5–2	2–2.5	2.5–3	3 Plus
Per cent (300 readings)	1	20	48	22	3	3	3

and both crests and troughs extend for long distances along the strike without change. Most exposures do not permit the full length of crests to be determined, but measurements of several hundred specimens indicate that 68 per cent have crests that extend for at least 10 inches as straight ridges. Fourteen per cent of the ripple crests examined extend more than 20 inches without appreciable change, and one specimen extends 42 inches.

The typical parallel ripple mark of the Moenkopi formation is asymmetrical and has an index (ratio of wave length to amplitude) of less than 15, which has been shown by various geologists (Twenhofel, 1939, p. 528) to be typical of water, and not of wind currents. Table 10 shows the distribution by per cent of ripple indices based on the measurements of 300 specimens. The results of related size studies shown in Tables 11 and 12 indicate that the average wave length of these ripple marks is between 1 and 1.5 inches and that the most common depth is $\frac{3}{32}$ to $\frac{1}{8}$ inch. The smallest well-developed set recorded measured an average of .2 inch from crest to crest; the largest 3.5 inches.

Variations in form and detail from the typical parallel, asymmetrical ripple mark are innumerable. One of the most common modifications is that in which the crests bifurcate at intervals of less than 10 inches to form an anastomosing pattern with ridges surrounding parallel rows of elongate depressions. Another is due to undulations of varying degree in the strike of the crests, resulting in a pattern that appears wavelike or undulating in plan view. Less numerous varieties are those resulting from combinations of the fundamental types, referred to as "imbricated or complex" by

Kindle (1917, p. 29) and as cross-ripple by Twenhofel (1939, p. 526). An example in which a set of symmetrical ripple marks was later altered by current ripples moving at right angles to form rows of irregular knobs has been collected. Another in which current ripple marks have had their troughs partitioned off into squares by the crests of wave marks, apparently after water had receded to a very shallow depth, is illustrated in Plate 7A. Various other combinations have been observed and recorded by the writer, and two types from the Moenkopi of San Rafael Swell, Utah, have been illustrated and discussed by Stokes (1950, p. 154).

Symmetrical, oscillation ripple marks are far less numerous in the Moenkopi formation than the parallel current-formed type, but they occur in the same shaly siltstones. Baker (1933, p. 36; 1936, p. 44) records their presence in the Moab and the Monument Valley areas in Utah, and the writer has observed them in various places along the Little Colorado Valley, Arizona. Kindle (1917, p. 48) has attempted to show that symmetrical ripple marks are largely confined to lacustrine deposits because current action "is generally absent or comparatively rare in lakes," while in the shallow seas "the product of the joint action of wave and current on sand is invariably the asymmetric ripple." Johnson (1938, p. 505) points out, however, that the supposed restriction of oscillation ripples to lacustrine deposits is very doubtful and cites his own observations on excellent symmetrical ripples on tidal flats bordering Long Island. Evidence furnished by the Moenkopi formation, where current- and wave-type ripple marks are in the same series of sediments and, indeed, in a few places occur on the same rock surface, one superimposed on the other, supports the contention of Johnson.

Two varieties of symmetrical ripple marks recently described by Evans (1943, p. 37) have been found in the Moenkopi formation. A double-crested or paired ripple mark was noted in several localities near Cameron, Arizona, in the upper red member. It has the appearance of alternate wide and narrow ripples. This form is interpreted by Evans as the result of the surges of passing waves being stronger in one direction than in the other with the result that a line of sand, like a small windrow, moves from the crest down the side of an already formed ripple mark. If returning surges are not sufficiently strong to carry the sand back, a double crest builds up.

A second variety of oscillation ripple mark (Pl. 6C) was found in the Wupatki member, 30 miles south of Cameron, and has been described by Stokes (1950, p. 154, Pl. 2) from San Rafael Swell, Utah. It consists of small, secondary crests developed in the troughs of larger crests. According to Evans this feature is the result of decreasing wave size where the reciprocating movement on the bottom is about half that which formed the original ripples.

Shaly siltstones of the Moenkopi contain in some localities various types of sedimentary structures associated with parallel ripple marks. Polygons formed by shrinkage cracks (Pls. 6A, 7B) and, in one specimen, the casts of salt crystals have been found superimposed on rippled surfaces. Peabody (1948, p. 333) records tracks of the reptile *Rotodactylus* from a rippled mudstone. These indicate that at least locally the mud-flat surfaces were drained of water, allowing subaerial conditions to prevail temporarily. On the other hand, the common lack of such structures on rippled surfaces suggests that in most places mud-flat layers were developed one on top of another without exposure to the atmosphere. Worm borings that may have been formed either under water or above are also associated with parallel ripple marks.

RIPPLE MARKS CHARACTERISTIC OF STREAM DEPOSITS: In massive siltstones and fine sandstones of the Moenkopi formation a variety of ripple mark very different from the parallel type in the shaly siltstones is common. It consists, in general, of irregular rows of crescent-shaped ridges and adjoining depressions giving a mammillated or cusplike appearance (Pls. 4B, 6D). Many of the depressions are bowl-shaped or semibowl-shaped, but some are wider than long, and still others are tonguelike, with elongation in the direction of current movement. Individual crests and troughs are not only far more variable in shape than those of parallel ripples, but also they are considerably larger.

Ripple marks characteristic of the massive or thick-bedded sandstones of the Moenkopi are referred to as "cusp ripples" in this paper. The name "current mark" was used by Kindle (1917, p. 36) in discussing this type of ripple mark, and the term "linguoid ripple mark," used by Twenhofel (1939, p. 524), probably also refers to this structure. Unfortunately Twenhofel does not illustrate or fully describe any examples.

Among several dozen specimens examined by the writer, the depression widths (measurements normal to flow direction) were mostly 2 to 6 inches, averaging about 5 inches; the ripple lengths (crest to crest) displayed a similar amount of variation and a similar average; the amplitudes were mostly between $\frac{1}{4}$ and $\frac{3}{4}$ inch. A ripple index is difficult to obtain accurately for this type because of wide variation within individual sets; however, those measured had a range between 6 and 15, which is similar to indices for other types of water-current ripple marks.

The origin of cusp ripple marks was a matter of speculation among various early geologists, several of whom failed to recognize the relationship of this structure to true ripple marks and attributed it to flows of mud (Hall, 1843; Owen, 1852). Jukes (1872), however, describes the marks as rippled surfaces "where the current was troubled." Considerably later, Kindle (1917) in his classic paper on ripple marks shows excellent illustrations of this type of structure from modern tidal currents and small brooks and in ancient rocks, and states that it forms "when converging currents meet or, where owing to irregular contour of the bottom or sides of the channel, variable or irregular currents are developed . . . ."

In the Moenkopi formation the characteristic association of cusp ripple marks with thick, massive beds of relatively coarse material and the comparative scarcity of these ripple marks among fine shaly siltstones suggest their development under strong current action. Doubtless they result from irregular and fluctuating streams, thus representing a distinctly different environment from that in which the parallel type of ripple mark was formed.

Relatively scarce in the Moenkopi, and apparently confined to the thick-bedded siltstones and sandstones, are intricate, small-scale structures known as interference ripple marks (Fig. 17). These are considered to have been caused by the interruption or breaking up of ripple action to form a cell-like pattern of tiny but deep pits within a network of rounded or elliptical ridges. Kindle (1917, p. 34) described them as being formed in water having a depth of a few inches or less and being common around the ends of bars, piers, or stranded logs, never along straight uninterrupted shore lines.

The writer has observed them in shallow waters where cross currents are active along streams.

INTERPRETATION OF RIPPLE ENVIRONMENTS: Attention has already been called to contrasts between the red, argillaceous shaly siltstone beds with their abundance of parallel ripple marks, and the thicker, more massive siltstones and sandstones that

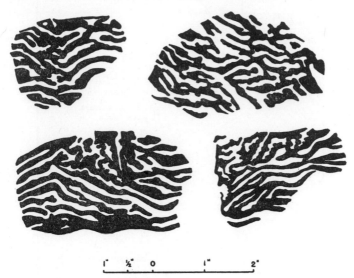

FIGURE 17.—*Pattern of interference ripple marks from stream deposits of Wupatki member, Moenkopi formation, at Citadel Sink, Arizona*

contain most of the cusp ripple marks. Many features of the former tend to confirm the conclusion that they were formed on extensive, mud-flat surfaces; likewise clear evidence indicates that the latter are the products of active and fluctuating stream currents.

The mud flats on which the shaly siltstones were formed may have been either tidal flats or river flood plains. The testimony of the various associated structures, however, strongly favors the theory of tidal flats. The many hundreds of individual layers, each with its surface covered by parallel ripple marks, suggest a constantly repeated advance and retreat of shallow waters across these surfaces—a feature more compatible with the regular movements of tide waters than with the irregular flood-ings of a stream. Furthermore, a remarkable constancy of direction in flow over wide areas is indicated by statistical studies of these ripples (Fig. 18) and supports the idea of a uniform retreat of waters across flat surfaces toward some branch of the sea. Similar uniformly rippled surfaces, covering many miles, may be observed today in Cholla Bay, Sonora, and at the lower end of the Colorado River delta, after each withdrawal of tide waters. The presence of symmetrical or wave ripples on these sur-faces also is in accord with the concept of tidal floods.

The testimony of structures other than ripple marks also favors the theory of an origin on tidal flats. In a number of localities and at many horizons, shrinkage cracks and salt casts are common, indicating that the beds containing them were at least temporarily above water, yet extremely few tracks of vertebrate animals have been found on the siltstone surfaces. Trails and borings of worms and other invertebrates (Brady, 1935, p. 11) are locally common, but plant remains are rare or absent despite

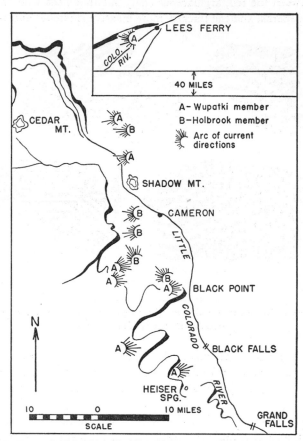

FIGURE 18.—*Map of current directions as indicated by average of ripple-mark readings in (a) Wupatki member and (b) Holbrook member, Moenkopi formation, northeastern Arizona*

Pointer lines radiating out from arcs indicate relative amounts and directions of current movements as indicated by ripple marks.

the fact that these deposits would make excellent media for preservation. Numerous salt casts suggest salinity of the water.

In contrast to the red shaly siltstones, the thick-bedded siltstones and sandstones are characterized by cross-stratification, cusp ripples, and coarser texture. All these features indicate constantly fluctuating current action. In addition many of the beds contain mud pellets and other locally derived fragments including those of amphibian or reptile bones. Most of the few plant remains of the formation, such as stems of reeds, are found in these beds. The footprints of reptiles, for which the formation is noted, are cast in some of them, but these tracks were actually formed in the mud of crumbly mudstones that underlie the massive beds in most places. In contrast, a majority of the amphibian skeletal remains and all known amphibian footprints of the Moenkopi are preserved in these stream deposits.

A third main type of detrital sediment is a deep red-brown mudstone that is structureless and so brittle that it normally crumbles with weathering to form very weak slopes or undercuts. Were it not for excellent casts of upper surfaces preserved on overlying siltstones, nothing would be known of the original structures in these mudstones. As it is, there is a clear record of large shrinkage cracks, of reptile tracks, and of current crescents that presumably were once very abundant over the surface. The very fine texture of the mudstone suggests that much of it may have formed from settling of clay and silt, in quiet water; there is no evidence that ripple marks formed on it.

FLOW MARKS

The term "flow mark" is used to designate types of irregular surface markings that apparently are developed through flowage of semiliquid sediment. The marks may be related to structures referred to by Twenhofel (1939, p. 561) as "current marks," though the latter are described as the products of erosion, whereas flow marks are primarily features of deposition. Both flow marks and current marks are considered the result of ebbing currents of water on mud flats, either tidal or fluvial.

Flow marks, not common in the Moenkopi formation, have been found in thin, shaly siltstones in several localities. One variety from the vicinity of Cameron, Arizona, and also from near Bears Ears in eastern Utah, consists of irregular, rounded lumps varying in width up to half an inch and rudely connected in a branching pattern (Pl. 9A). A second variety, found in abundance near Flagstaff, Arizona, is finer and more delicate; it consists of narrow ridges with dendritic pattern that spread downcurrent like the distributaries of a stream (Pl. 9C).

The fine, linear ridges constituting the second type of flow mark are associated with very small interference ripple marks on some surfaces and appear to have developed from them where water draining off caused flows of muddy silt to build outward. In one specimen a clearly developed current crescent merges downstream into spreading flow marks (Pl. 9B).

The principal significance of flow marks in the Moenkopi formation is the evidence they give concerning the conditions of development. They suggest that mud-flat surfaces were being drained of shallow waters and that a continental environment prevailed where they were being formed.

CURRENT CRESCENTS

The term "current crescent" has been applied by Peabody (1947, p. 73) to semicircular or "U" shaped ridges developed on surfaces believed to have been those of ancient mud flats. It is a variety of "current mark" as defined by Twenhofel (1939, p. 561). The crescents in some places are arranged in groups oriented in similar direction, but elsewhere they occur singly. They range from 3 to 5 cm. in width, and their "horns" point in the direction of current movement.

Current crescents are interpreted by Peabody as the markings formed by a sheet of water eddying around some stranded object such as a clay pebble or piece of wood. Where the current is stronger on one side than the other, the resulting horn is longer.

Observations of modern examples indicate that they are developed during the last stages of flow. This idea is substantiated in ancient specimens by the fact that both the stranded objects and the furrowed mud were not washed away, but hardened by subsequent desiccation before permanent burial.

In the Moenkopi formation the natural casts of current crescents are not uncommon locally (Pl. 9B). Although the mud surfaces on which the crescents were originally developed normally are destroyed because the material is crumbly, overlying strata of resistant sandstone or siltstone have preserved an excellent record in reverse. In some examples studied, the character of the stranded debris that caused the crescent has been determined by the shape of its imprint. In many places, the direction of former current movement has been ascertained by the orientation of the markings.

Peabody (1947, p. 76) observed that footprints of a large species of the reptile, *Chirotherium*, found associated with current crescents, indicate that this animal "habitually travelled up and down stream channels but not across them." He describes and illustrates examples from the Little Colorado River area showing the relationship of the crescents to various animal trackways.

CASTS OF SALT CRYSTALS

Casts of cubic salt crystals are locally numerous in red beds at several horizons in the Moenkopi formation. They give evidence of the subaerial origin of the deposits containing them and they indicate intense evaporation.

Moenkopi salt casts range in size from $1/16$ inch up to a maximum of about $3/4$ inch. Most of them are composed of red or green, argillaceous mudstone and appear partly submerged in shaly beds of the same composition (Pl. 10C). The scattered cubes are variously oriented. Some show only a single corner projecting above the mudstone surface, others have an entire margin with two corners tilted up, and still others include a complete face raised as a rectangular platform. In one specimen salt casts were formed projecting through a ripple-marked surface; in another they were associated with shrinkage cracks. In most places, however, they are scattered over otherwise smooth, flat siltstone surfaces.

Salt casts of the Moenkopi formation have been found in abundance in two localities along Echo Cliffs, in a section south of Cameron, and in one near Meteor Crater, Arizona. At all these sites they are in the basal (Wupatki) member, and at one, Cedar Ridge near Echo Cliffs, they are also present in the middle slope unit. Gregory and Moore (1931, p. 48) report salt casts "in a few places" in the region of Circle Cliffs, Utah. Peabody (1948, p. 302) describes them from the Holbrook member at a locality northwest of Cameron where, he states, they are associated with the cast footprints of lacertoid reptiles.

RAIN PITS

Rain pits, relatively uncommon in the Moenkopi formation, have been recorded from red beds in such widely separated areas as the Valley of Fire, Nevada (Longwell, 1928, p. 47), near Virgin City in western Utah (Gregory, Personal communication, 1948), along the Colorado River at Crescent Wash, southeastern Utah (Longwell *et al.*, 1923, p. 18), and in Monument Valley, eastern Utah (Baker, 1936, p. 44). Specimens from Wupatki (Pl. 10A), Cameron, and the Little Colorado Valley at Crack-in-the-Rock, Arizona, have been examined by the writer. The record from Nevada in which rain pits are reported from about the middle of the formation (bed 10) and that from western Utah in the lower red member (bed 15) are of particular interest because they demonstrate an extension of subaerial conditions westward into the geosyncline when those red beds were formed.

All the rain-pit specimens examined were in thin, shaly siltstones, and about half of them on ripple-marked surfaces. The pits range in diameter from $\frac{1}{16}$ to $\frac{1}{4}$ inch, are circular, and show typical projecting rims. The craters appear scattered over silt-stone surfaces, with many of them coalescing. Possibly specimens would be far more numerous if the structureless claystones of the formation were also good media for preservation. As it is, these rocks are very brittle and normally crumble into tiny particles upon weathering, thus eliminating all possibility of preserving surface marks except where casts have been made in overlying siltstones or sandstones.

CORE-AND-SHELL STRUCTURE IN MUD

The term "core-and-shell" is applied to a structure developed in massive, silty mudstone where structureless rounded cores of various shapes are surrounded by series of concentric shells or layers, each with a thickness ranging from $\frac{1}{8}$ to $\frac{1}{2}$ inch (Pl. 8, A–D). The cores or central lumps range in size from 1 or 2 inches up to at least 12 inches. They are concretionary in appearance, assuming the wide range of forms typical of many concretions. The simpler forms are ovoid or pie-shaped, but more complex varieties are best described as mammilary or reniform. Still other types are elongate to the extent that they have a rude resemblance to bones and have been mistaken for them by the uninitiated. In 1940 a truck load of cores from near Gap Trading Post, Arizona, was presented to the Museum of Northern Arizona by a well driller who believed that he had fossils of vertebrate animals.

The outer layers or shells, which readily peel from the cores, superficially give the appearance of beds that have been much deformed and contorted. Such an explanation is untenable, however, because the parting planes pass completely around the cores. Structures of this type have been observed in the process of forming on mud flats of the Colorado delta and are described under the name of "pseudo-bedding" (McKee, 1939, p. 81). They appear to be due to shrinkage in uniform, structureless masses of mud and are brought about by drainage of water from the surface of the area. They are characteristic of subaerial conditions, following flooding, in a region of considerable aridity.

In the Moenkopi formation silty mudstone beds with core-and-shell structure extending for at least several hundred yards have been found in several widely separated localities. At Bears Ears, Utah, they occur at the top of a 3-foot bed above the fish-bearing strata. At Citadel Ruins near the Little Colorado, Arizona, they appear in the Wupatki member, 50 feet above the base of the formation, but 10 miles north, near Black Point, they are in the middle member. At Cedar Ridge Trading Post near Echo Cliffs, Arizona, they are also common, and west of St. George, Utah, they occur in a calcareous siltstone in the middle of the Virgin limestone member (Poborski, Personal communication, 1951).

SHRINKAGE CRACKS

Shrinkage cracks in mudstones and siltstones of the Moenkopi formation furnish clear evidence that the deposits in which they occur were formed in a subaerial environment. Because the formation includes both marine and continental beds as

TABLE 13.—*Areas and horizons from which shrinkage cracks have been reported*

	Upper red	Middle red	Virgin limestone	Lower red	Undiffer-entiated
W. St. George, Utah, Poborski (Personal communication)........................	....	....	×	....	....
San Rafael Swell, Gilluly and Reeside (1928) Baker (1946).............................	....	....	....	....	×
Moab, Baker et al. (1927).....................	....	....	....	....	×
Indian Creek, McKee (this paper)..............	....	....	....	....	×
Monument Valley, Baker (1936)................	....	....	....	....	×
Kaiparowits, Gregory and Moore (1931).........	....	....	....	....	×
Little Colorado Valley, McKee (this paper)......	×	×	....	....	....
Echo Cliffs, McKee (this paper)................	×	×	....	....	....
Central Kane County, Gregory (1948)..........	....	....	....	×	....
Virgin Valley, Gregory (1952)..................	×	×	....	×	....
Zion Natl. Monument, Gregory and Williams (1947)................................	....	....	....	×	....

shown by its flora and fauna, evidence on the environment of particular groups of red beds is especially significant. Thus, Baker (1946, p. 58), in discussing the shaly beds above the marine limestones in the Green River Desert, states "the occurrence of 'fossil' mud cracks at several horizons shows that shallow water conditions prevailed and that the sediments were repeatedly exposed to the air." Likewise Gilluly and Reeside (1928), p. 65) refer to the "recurrence of mudcracks" as evidence of continental conditions in the upper main part of the formation in San Rafael Swell, Utah.

Although Moenkopi surfaces covered with shrinkage cracks are much less numerous than those marked by ripples, they have been reported from most of the areas in which this formation occurs and from at least four of its six members (Table 13). Although Longwell (1928, p. 46–52) does not mention shrinkage cracks in any of his Nevada sections, the distribution of the cracks in the Zion National Monument and Virgin Valley areas indicates that subaerial conditions are represented in all the red-bed members at least as far west as western Utah.

All the shrinkage cracks examined by the writer in the Moenkopi formation appear to have very irregular, reticulate patterns. Networks are composed of polygons that vary in number of sides, but most are either four- or five-sided. In some specimens the edges of the polygons are straight, but in many others they curve gently. A few specimens show branches that extend out from the network without any connections, tapering to narrow points. The size of the shrinkage cracks appears to be controlled largely by the type of sediment in which they formed. These include (1) thin, shaly, weak red siltstones, and also platy limestones, in which cracks average ¼ inch or less in width and are very shallow; and (2) structureless reddish-brown mudstones or claystones in which the cracks range up to an inch in width and may extend downward half an inch or more.

Shrinkage cracks in shaly siltstones and in silty limestones (Pl. 4C) are small and relatively uncommon, probably because the high percentage of silt tends to make the sediment noncohesive, and the thinness of the beds limits downward development of cracks. Also, possibly most of the silt deposits were not exposed to the air, and therefore desiccation would not have affected them. Current ripple marks are extremely common in the same type of rock, but ripples, unlike shrinkage cracks, may have been formed and preserved without being exposed to the atmosphere. A few specimens show shrinkage cracks superimposed upon current ripple marks (Pl. 6A, 7B); even fewer have the small cubic molds of salt crystals associated.

In the structureless red-brown mudstones of the Moenkopi, large shrinkage cracks may have been developed in great abundance, yet, due to the crumbly, brittle character of the rock, well-preserved cracks are seldom recognized. The record of their presence is almost invariably obtained through natural casts developed in massive overlying sandstone or siltstone. These ridgelike, reverse markings are conspicuous features on the undersides of many overhanging ledges, and in numerous places they are associated with the tracks of reptiles such as *Chirotherium* and *Rotodactylus* or with large ripple marks of the cusp type. Specimens found in the *Chirotherium barthi* quarry near Cameron, Arizona, and built into the walls of the trading post there are particularly striking examples of the characteristic, large, well-developed polygons.

Whether shrinkage cracks in red beds of the Moenkopi formation were developed on tidal flats, flood plains, or both is not known. Some specimens in which mud layers between the cracks tend to curl upward have been observed by Gregory (Personal communication, 1948) in southwestern Utah and by the writer along the Little Colorado Valley. This feature has been given as evidence of shrinkage under fresh-water conditions (Twenhofel, 1939, p. 540), but as applied to the Moenkopi does not appear to be sufficiently widespread or persistent to justify definite conclusions. The general spacing, depth, and width of the cracks appear to have been determined in large measure by the amount of silt present in the mud and by the thickness of the layers, although the rate of drying and other factors may also have been important.

In the Virgin limestone member west of St. George, Utah, beds containing marine faunas occur both subjacent and superjacent to limestone beds that contain shrinkage cracks. Doubtless these cracks developed during emergence and desiccation between periods of marine deposition, suggesting the general shallowness of the sea in which the limestone formed. Shrinkage cracks occur in some of the shaly siltstones of the Virgin limestone member.

FOSSILS

VERTEBRATE ANIMALS

The remains of vertebrate animals were noted in intraformational conglomerates of the Moenkopi formation near Holbrook, Arizona, more than 30 years ago (Gregory, 1917, p. 27). Also recorded by Gregory (1917, p. 35) are bones from near the top of the Moenkopi in the vicinity of Tucker Springs, north of Winslow, which were col-

TABLE 14.—*Key to vertebrate fossil horizons and localities recorded in measured sections* (Figs. 2–6)

Symbol	Section	Bed	Locality	Fauna
A	2	3	St. Johns	Reptile (?) skull
B	3	5	12 miles w. of Concho	Skull and interclavicles of amphibians
C	Welles Table 1	4	Holbrook	Fish spines and scales, bones of amphibians and reptiles (Described by Welles, 1947, p. 241–294), casts of *Chirotherium* tracks
D	5	8	Winslow	Bone fragments
E	5	14	Winslow	Capitosaurid-type skull and tracks, casts of *Chirotherium* tracks
F	5	16	Winslow	Capitosaurid-type skulls and skeleton, casts of *Chirotherium* tracks
G	6	3	Meteor Crater	Ganoid fish, some amphibian bones
H	6	4	Meteor Crater	Amphibian skulls (20 Capitosaurid type, 1 *Aphaneramma*-like amphibian)
I	6	5	Meteor Crater	Tracks of *Chirotherium* and *Rotodactylus*
J	13	4	E. Black Falls	Teeth of vertebrates
K	15	8	W. Black Falls	Bone fragments
L	15	8	W. Black Falls	Casts of *Chirotherium* tracks
M	16	3	Hwy. 89, Cameron	Amphibian skull (Welles, locality 71)
N	16	3	Hwy. 89, Cameron	Pelecypods
O	16	5	Hwy. 89, Cameron	Amphibian bones (Welles, localities 69, 70), plant remains
P	16	7	Hwy. 89, Cameron	*Chirotherium* track casts, Amphibian bones (Welles, locality 68a), plant fragments
Q	19	6	4.8 miles w. of Cameron	Vertebrate bone fragments
R	19	7	4.8 miles w. of Cameron	Vertebrate bone fragments
S	19	7	4.8 miles w. of Cameron	Amphibian and reptile bone fragments, fish bones and spines, pelecypod shells
T	19	8	4.8 miles w. of Cameron	*Cyclotosaurus*-type skulls (two)
U	18	6	Tappan Wash	Track casts, *Chirotherium barthi*
W	7	Above 1	Leupp	Fish

lected by E. C. Case. Among these was an interclavicle fragment identified as *Metoposaurus*, closely allied to *Metoposaurus frassi*. Subsequently the skull of a stegocephalian was discovered at an outcrop 9 miles south of Winslow by R. T. Bird and described as *Stanocephalosaurus birdi* by Brown (1933). Little was known of the Moenkopi fauna, however, until the summer of 1938, when S. P. Welles and C. L. Camp with a party from the University of California undertook the first of a series of explorations and quarrying operations for vertebrate remains in this formation.

The intensive program of research by Welles has brought to light a large and varied fauna of reptiles, amphibians, and fish in the Moenkopi of northeastern Arizona (Table 14). Excavations have been especially productive at localities (1) 6 miles west of Holbrook (Holbrook member), (2) in Moqui Wash west of Winslow (Wupatki member), (3) at Meteor Crater (Wupatki member), and (4) south and west of Cameron (Holbrook member). As yet only the material from the Holbrook quarry has been described (Welles, 1947), but the rest of the fauna is being prepared for study. Its composition and general character are briefly discussed in *A guide to the Continental Triassic of Northern Arizona* (Camp *et al.*, 1947).

TABLE 15.—*Vertebrate fauna of Moenkopi formation described from skeletal remains*

Group	Name	Member	Locality	Reference
Reptile	*Anisodontosaurus greeri*	Holbrook	W. of Holbrook	Welles, 1947
Reptile	*Arizonasaurus babbitti*	Holbrook	W. of Holbrook	Welles, 1947
Amphibian	*Stanocephalosaurus birdi*	Holbrook	S. of Winslow	Brown, 1933
Amphibian	*Taphrognathus bradyi*	Holbrook	W. of Holbrook	Welles, 1947
Amphibian	*Cyclotosaurus randalli*	Holbrook	W. of Holbrook	Welles, 1947
Amphibian	*Rhadalognathus boweni*	Holbrook	W. of Holbrook	Welles, 1947
Amphibian	*? Aphaneramma*	Wupatki	Meteor Crater	Camp *et al.*, 1947
Amphibian	*? Capitosaurus*	Wupatki	Meteor Crater	Camp *et al.*, 1947
Fish	Paleoniscids	Wupatki	Meteor Crater	Camp *et al.*, 1947
Fish	Paleoniscids	Holbrook	W. of Holbrook	Welles, 1947
Fish	Dipnoans	Holbrook	W. of Holbrook	Welles, 1947
Fish	Sharks	Holbrook	W. of Holbrook	Welles, 1947

In addition to the extensive collections from localities where quarries were established, Welles and his associates have obtained a reptile (?) skull from near St. Johns (sect. 2, bed 3[4]), several amphibian skulls and interclavicles from west of Concho (sect. 3, bed 5), an amphibian skull from the east side of Holbrook (Camp *et al.*, 1947, p. 6), near where Gregory first noted vertebrate remains, several skulls from the original R. T. Bird locality south of Winslow, fish remains near Leupp (sect. 7, above bed 1), and fragmentary bones in the limestone conglomerates west of Black Point (sect. 15, bed 8) and elsewhere in the area. Searches north and west of the Little Colorado area have been far less successful. Exceptions are some good fish remains from the Bears Ears of southeastern Utah (sect. 37, bed 3); amphibian bones (sect. 37, bed 6) from the same section; and vertebrate remains from Lavender Canyon near Indian Creek (sect. 38, bed 6). Bone fragments are reported from the "red beds" divisions of Zion Monument area, southwestern Utah, by Gregory and Williams (1947, p. 226).

A very incomplete list of the Moenkopi fauna, based upon forms thus far described from skeletal remains, includes two reptiles, six amphibians, and three fish types (Table 15). The amphibians not only are represented by more varieties than are the reptiles, but also by far more and better-preserved individuals. This is in contrast to the record of footprints (Peabody, 1948, p. 318), where reptilian trackways are abundant but those of amphibians rare. Apparently the massive, cross-stratified sandstones and siltstones that contain most of the amphibian remains were formed under stream-current conditions in an environment not favorable to reptiles, which crossed the mud-flat areas, as shown by their tracks.

---

[4] Refers to measured sections in this paper. *See also* Table 14.

In 1947 a detailed examination was made of strata at the fossil quarry developed by S. P. Welles and party 6 miles south of Cameron, Arizona. Quarrying operations were along an east-west extending ledge for about 70 feet. Excavations exposed a series of rock types (Fig. 19) representing wide variation in lithology and considerable lensing and lateral change in individual beds. Analysis of the section shows the results of fluctuation in deposition and development of numerous diastems. It indicates a

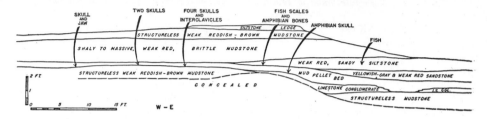

FIGURE 19.—*Cross section of fossil quarry 6 miles south of Cameron, Arizona*
All skulls found just at surface indicated. Compiled from field sketch.

lack of fossils in structureless mudstones that probably formed under quiet-water conditions and a concentration of skeletal material, together with mud pellets, among current-formed deposits. Rapid burial in a channel favorable for concentration of debris doubtless was a significant factor in the development of this fossil accumulation.

Other fossil localities have not been analyzed with corresponding care; however, most of them are in massive siltstone or sandstone beds of a type considered to have been formed by active stream currents. Six miles west of Holbrook at the site described by Welles (1947, p. 242), bones occur above a thick series of shaly mudstones and are associated with clay pellets, limestone pebbles, and plant remains at the base of a thick sandstone unit. At a site 5 miles west of Cameron, two amphibian skulls were embedded in a thick, cross-laminated sandstone, near the base where it rested on a shaly mudstone. Various other fossil occurrences show a similar relationship to stream-deposited sandstones. One notable exception is at Meteor Crater, where 20 amphibian skulls of the capitosaurid type and a slender-snouted variety similar to *Aphaneramma* were obtained from a bed of silty limestone, overlain by shaly siltstones containing fish remains (Camp *et al.*, 1947, p. 7).

TRACKWAYS OF VERTEBRATE ANIMALS

In the Valley of Fire near Overton, Nevada, the tracks of small reptiles preserved in calcareous shaly mudstones of the Moenkopi formation were reported (but not described) by Longwell in 1928 (p. 45). This is the first record of the footprints of vertebrate animals from the Moenkopi.

In the Little Colorado River region numerous series of tracks, representing two distinct types of animals, were illustrated and briefly described by Brady in 1935 (p. 11). The larger type he recognizes as similar to *Chirotherium* of the Buntsandstein in Germany. The smaller, subsequently named *Rotodactylus*, he describes as the track of a very small unidentified reptile, having a backward-projecting spur to its footprint and a tendency toward bipedality. He considers that this track was made by a slender, dinosaurlike reptile.

For several years, starting in 1938, a very intensive and careful study of the trackways of vertebrate animals in the Moenkopi formation was conducted by Mr. Frank Peabody, then of the University of California. His investigation brought to light

TABLE 16.—*Localities not previously recorded where trackways of vertebrate animals have been found in the Moenkopi formation*

Locality	Bed	Section no. (Described this paper)
Shinumo Altar, Arizona...................	13	25
12 mi. nw. Cameron, Arizona..............	4	20
2½ mi. w. Navajo Bridge, Arizona.........	1, 2	29
Monument Valley, Arizona................	4	35
Bears Ears, Utah........................	4	37
Lavender Canyon, Utah..................	4	38
Paria, Utah............................	....	Noted by Camp (1951)
Capitol Reef, Utah......................	....	Noted by Peabody (1950)
Vernal, Utah...........................	....	Noted by Peabody (1946)

large numbers of footprints from many localities and several horizons within the formation. In a monograph (Peabody, 1948) he describes the fauna, its environmental significance, and its value for correlation purposes. Outstanding general conclusions are summarized here.

The vertebrate fauna of the Moenkopi formation as known from the record of trackways consists of a large number and variety of reptiles and a few amphibians. The amphibian tracks are referred to the genus *Capitosaurus*. The reptiles include eight species of *Chirotherium*, three of *Rotodactylus*, and several lacertoid types— *i.e.*, those having lizardlike body form.

Most of the trackways studied by Peabody came from northeastern Arizona. Localities where they are especially abundant are Cameron, Meteor Crater, Moqui Wash west of Winslow, and a hill 5 miles west of Holbrook. They have been found at many other localities (Table 16) and according to Peabody (Personal communication, 1951) are present at every major locality where skeletal remains have been found. In southern Utah trackways have been noted at Bears Ears, Capitol Reef, Hurricane, Rockville, and Paria.

The types of environment in which various trackways of the Moenkopi were developed have been given careful consideration by Peabody (1948, p. 317–318, 411–412). He notes that amphibian tracks are absent from the surfaces of former mud flats, whereas reptile tracks are common on these. On the other hand, he records amphibian but not reptilian footprints among sandstone deposits believed to represent former sand spits. Thus, he concludes that the amphibians lived in and around rivers but did not venture out on the mud flats where reptiles were abundant. Peabody further observes that tracks of the reptile *Chirotherium* appear to be remarkably consistent in orientation, indicating directions of travel parallel to those of water-current movement, but not across the channels. He interprets this as indicating that the animals used direct routes of travel and did not wander about on the mud flats, which furnished little food or shelter.

Evidences of the age of the Moenkopi furnished by its trackways are interesting but far from conclusive. Certain Moenkopi chirotheriids—*C. minus* and *C. barthi*—are found also in the Upper Buntsandstein of Germany as pointed out by Peabody (1948, p. 413), yet he shows that another variety, *C. marshalli*, "seems most closely related to a form from the early Middle Keuper of England." Some of the lacertoid reptile footprints that locally occur in countless numbers are said to resemble *Akropus* of the German Buntsandstein (Peabody, 1948, p. 323); however, very similar trackways are recorded from the Italian ? Keuper. Thus, attempts to correlate the fossil footprints of the Moenkopi with corresponding European types merely indicate an Early or Medial Triassic age.

Trackways described thus far from the Moenkopi appear to represent the upper part of the formation as measured in terms of the most extensive sections in southwestern Utah. *Rotadactylus mckeei* from Hurricane, Utah, and *Chirotherium* cf. *moquiensis* from Rockville, Utah, were found in the upper red member of the Moenkopi. The many specimens described from the Little Colorado Valley of Arizona are partly from the basal or Wupatki member, but, as indicated earlier in this paper on the basis of field studies, these members are stratigraphically equivalent to the upper part of the formation (above the Virgin limestone member) in the southwestern Utah area. The *Rotadactylus* trackway from the upper red member at Hurricane is like that from the Wupatki member at Meteor Crater, and the *Chirotherium* from Rockville is like *C. moquiensis* from the Wupatki member at Winslow (Peabody, Personal communication, 1951).

The horizons represented by the described trackways in the Moenkopi formation indicate a stratigraphic position well above the *Meekoceras* or middle Lower Triassic zone and largely or entirely above the *Tirolites* zone (upper part of the Lower Triassic) of the Virgin limestone member. This suggests that they represent a time either late in the Early Triassic or possibly early in the Medial Triassic.

TRACKS AND TRAILS OF INVERTEBRATES

The record of varied forms of invertebrate life, preserved as tracks and trails in continental deposits of the Moenkopi formation, was first brought to light through the work of L. F. Brady (1935, p. 11), who describes several types of trails and illustrates one. Six principal varieties, including some recently discovered, are recognized to date. The following summary of these has been prepared with the aid of Mr. Brady.

"Fucoid"-like fillings of borings, 5 to 10 mm. in diameter, many of which pass through laminae and some of which are in vertical positions (Pl. 12B), are locally numerous in shaly siltstones of the Moenkopi formation. A few of these fillings show faint traces of pellet structure and may have been formed as the egested material left by annelids. In general, the casts have been referred to as "worm borings" or "worm trails." In Utah at Zion National Monument (Gregory and Williams, 1947, p. 225) they occur in the lower red member, and in Arizona among younger strata at St. Johns (Section 2, bed 2), west of Shadow Mountain (Section 21, bed 7), and at various places near Cameron.

A type of small (1 mm. wide) meandering trail, developed on bedding surfaces of siltstone (Pl. 11B), likewise is attributed to the movements of worms. Such trails consist of median grooves with raised edges. Specimens of these from Tappan Wash near Cameron, Arizona, occur at the same horizon as reptile (*Chirotherium barthi*) footprints.

Tracks attributed to arthropods found at the fossil quarry near Meteor Crater, Arizona, consist of series of impressions in two parallel rows about 1 cm. apart. The impressions vary from oval to crescentic, and they are about 3 to 5 mm. apart. Other tracks considered to have been made by arthropods are from basal Moenkopi beds east of Flagstaff, Arizona (Pl. 12A). These were made by 8-footed animals very similar to the scorpion-like forms represented in the Coconino sandstone (Brady, 1947, p. 466–470). Each trackway is 26 to 30 mm. wide and consists of a double line of foot impressions. Each group of three or four foot impressions makes an angle of about 45° with the line of travel.

Certain other trails of invertebrate animals from the quarry east of Flagstaff are interpreted by Brady as possibly the marks made by small crustaceans swimming in very shallow water. They consist of long series of delicate marks spreading V-shaped from a central line like the hairs on a fox's tail (Pl. 11A).

A form of cast of uncertain origin but very similar to markings from the German Bunter described as *Isopodicnus* sp. (Schindewolf, 1928) is added to this list of probable invertebrate animal tracks. It appears as a series of small rounded mounds, each about 15 mm. by 10 mm. and divided in the center by a notch or groove. The grooves are all oriented in one direction, but mounds are not evenly spaced as are footprints. Faint transverse corrugations appear on each mound. These casts have been interpreted as possible isopod impressions, but this classification is open to question. They occur in the fossil quarry at Meteor Crater, Arizona.

All these track types are represented in the collection at the Museum of Northern Arizona. An excellent trackway from Capitol Reef, Utah, said to be that of a *Limulus*, is reported by Peabody (Personal communication, 1951) to have been collected by a Mr. Kelley of that locality.

PLANTS

Traces of plant life have been noted at various horizons and in many parts of the Moenkopi formation, but nearly all specimens are poorly preserved and so fragmentary as to be indeterminate. Furthermore, considering the thickness and extent of continental deposits in this formation and the diversity of amphibian and reptilian life represented by trackways and skeletal remains, the record of plant life seems extremely poor and incomplete.

Most plant fossils in the Moenkopi consist of impressions, especially of stems. At two Arizona localities, in Moqui Wash near Winslow and at Cameron, a few specimens of petrified wood occur. In the Zion Monument area of Utah "a few bits of wood" were obtained by Gregory and Williams (1947, p. 226). Reeds and *Equiseta* are the principal plants recognized, but coniferous twigs are reported by Ward (1905, p. 29), and a species resembling *Walchia gracilis* from the type locality of the Moenkopi on the Little Colorado River is mentioned by Gregory (1917, p. 25).

Nearly all the plant specimens recorded are from the northeastern Arizona region. They are listed by Gregory (1917, p. 24–26) from Moenkopi Wash, Grand Falls, and near Holbrook and are included in measured sections by the writer from Winslow (sect. 5, bed 12), west of Black Point (sect. 15, bed 8), south of Cameron (sect. 16, beds 5, 7), Poverty Tank (sect. 17, bed 4), and Tappan Wash (sect. 18, bed 6). In most of these localities they are associated with mud pellets, casts of reptile tracks, and worm trails. Plant fragments also have been recorded from Salt Valley, Utah (Dane, 1935, p. 43), Bears Ears, Utah (sect. 37, bed 5), and in the Zion Park Area, Utah (Gregory, 1952, p. 62).

MARINE INVERTEBRATE FOSSILS

Invertebrate fossils are abundant and moderately varied among limestones and calcareous shaly mudstones in marine members of the Moenkopi formation. In most places they are poorly preserved, however, and they have received so little study that not much is known concerning them or their significance. Pelecypods are represented by the greatest numbers, both of individuals and of species, though gastropods are also very common. Brachiopods are common in some beds, but are largely of nondiagnostic, long-ranging types. Ammonites, though scarce in most sections, furnish the best means of age determination. Crinoid joints are abundant at some horizons, starfish have been recorded (Longwell, 1928, p. 45), and ostracods are present (Gilluly and Reeside, 1928, p. 66; Gregory and Moore, 1931, p. 52; Poborski, 1953, p. 79). A collection of interesting marine arthropods, belonging to the crustacean genus *Halicyne*, has recently been made by Poborski (1953, p. 79) in the Virgin limestone member of southwestern Utah.

The first marine invertebrate fossils reported from beds of the Moenkopi formation are the pelecypods "*Pleurophorus, Schizodus,* and *Bakewellia*" collected by Gilbert (1875, p. 161, 177) from Kanab Valley 3 miles below Fredonia, Arizona. He suggests correlation with "the Permo-Carboniferous of the Mississippi Valley." A few years later this area was studied in some detail by Walcott (1880, p. 223), who recognized two divisions in the strata (Moenkopi) between the cherty limestones, now known as Kaibab, and the Shinarump conglomerate. In his lower division Walcott recognizes 4 pelecypods, 2 gastropods, and 1 cephalopod; from the upper he lists 23 genera and 34 species of invertebrates. Twenty of the species he considers have strong Paleozoic relations; 10 of them, all pelecypods, he states have marked Permian character; and 2 forms, notably *Pentacrinus*, are of typical Mesozoic type. He concludes that this fauna represents the Permian age.

Invertebrate fossils collected during a traverse from Lees Ferry to Toroweap and Hurricane by Shimer (1919) included 43 species from the Moenkopi formation. Shimer notes (1) the absence of the most typical Permian genera, (2) the reduction of brachiopods and increase of pelecypods characteristic of the Triassic, and (3) the presence of typical Triassic forms; therefore he considers the Moenkopi Lower Triassic. A similar conclusion was reached by Girty from studies of extensive collections made by Reeside and Bassler (1922, p. 68) and by Gregory (1952, p. 63) throughout northwestern Arizona and southwestern Utah.

The abundance and variety of marine fossils in the Moenkopi formation increase greatly toward the area of thickest sections in southwestern Utah. Furthermore, nearly all the fossils in that area are within two main stratigraphic units —the Timpoweap at the base and the Virgin limestone member several hundred feet above. A few poorly preserved brachiopods, pelecypods, and gastropods have been collected by Gregory in the Shnabkaib, 60 to 160 feet above its base, at North Creek near Virgin City, Utah (John B. Reeside, Jr., personal communication, 1953).

In the Timpoweap is found the ammonite *Meekoceras* (Reeside and Bassler, 1922, p. 67; Gregory, 1948, p. 227), a fact which indicates that that member is correlative with the world-wide *Meekoceras* zone at the middle of the Lower Triassic. The younger fauna of the Virgin limestone is being studied by Poborski. Cephalopods collected largely by him have been examined by Muller (Personal communication, September 6, 1951), who states that they represent the *Tirolites* zone, which is near the top of the Lower Triassic. They include *Tirolites spinosus* Mojs., orthocerids, *Cordillerites?* sp., and *Hungarites?* sp.

Eastward from the thick sections of southwestern Utah, fossil-bearing beds of the Timpoweap extend as far as Kaibab Gulch (Gregory, 1948, p. 227), and those of the Virgin limestone member as far as Fredonia (Section 33). In central Utah, the seaway apparently extended much farther east, at least during the time represented by the *Meekoceras* zone. Marine fossils, mostly pelecypods, are reported from sandy limestone beds near Fruita (Gregory and Moore, 1931, p. 52). Farther north, fossils from the Sinbad limestone at three places in San Rafael Swell include 30 species and varieties as recognized by Girty (Gilluly and Reeside, 1928, p. 66). In addition to pelecypods, gastropods, echinoids, and ostracods, they include *Meekoceras gracilitatis*. Farther east in the Green River Valley a small fauna including *Meekoceras?* sp. has been reported (Baker *et al.*, 1927, p. 797; McKnight, 1940, p. 58). This is the easternmost known occurrence of marine invertebrates in the Moenkopi formation.

At several localities in northeastern Arizona pelecypods have been found in the Moenkopi formation, but they are believed to be fresh- or brackish-water types. They appear as concentrations of a single species in thin limestone lenses or beds of local distribution, and they are closely associated with red beds considered of continental origin. Typical examples of these mollusk concentrations are west of Cameron (sect. 19, bed 7) and near Black Point (sect. 15, bed 8).

Basic problems concerned with the invertebrate faunas of the Moenkopi are that (1) many, perhaps most, of the species are undescribed; (2) no standard for comparison is available for most of the fauna, other than ammonites; (3) the state of preservation of most of the fossils, especially in the Virgin limestone member where they are largely internal molds, is poor; and (4) in much collecting done in the past, specimens from various horizons have not been differentiated, and even the faunas of the Timpoweap and Virgin members have been confused.

ENVIRONMENT OF MOENKOPI

CLIMATE

A wide difference of opinion exists concerning the type or types of climate that prevailed during the Triassic period. A common viewpoint (Schuchert and Dunbar,

1941, p. 314) is that "on the whole, arid or semi-arid climate seems to have been remarkably widespread." In contrast, Moore (1949, p. 309) states that the nature of plant and animal life and the existence of many sluggish streams and shallow bodies argue against widespread arid or semiarid climate. He concludes that "probably both in eastern and western North America, temperate climates, characterized by alternate wet and dry seasons, prevailed."

A comparison of Lower Triassic deposits with those of the Upper Triassic in western North America suggests the inadvisability of making generalizations concerning the climate, even for this one region, for such a long span of time. The Lower Triassic as indicated by the Moenkopi sediments was a time of general low relief, whereas Upper Triassic conglomerates of the Shinarump and Chinle formations show that areas of considerable elevation then bordered the depositional basin. Furthermore, extensive gypsum deposits and a general scarcity of land plants in the Moenkopi are features not common to later Triassic sediments. Thus, both types of climate that have been suggested for Triassic time may have existed in western North America.

In the Moenkopi formation the abundance of large reptiles such as *Chirotherium*, represented by their trackways, and of big, sluggish amphibians[5], the skulls of which are numerous in the massive sandstones, suggests a continuously warm climate, unbroken by seasons of cold. Plant remains, unfortunately, furnish no evidence on this subject, for they are uncommon, poorly preserved, and are represented almost entirely by such stream-inhabiting types as reeds and scouring rushes. Marine invertebrate fossils, on the other hand, give some support to the concept of a warm climate through the abundance of crinoid joints in certain beds of the Virgin limestone member.

Sediments and sedimentary structures in the Moenkopi suggest a semiarid or arid climate. Although red beds that make up much of the formation are probably the result of alternate wetting and drying, as shown by Krynine (1949, p. 61), and therefore lend no support to the concept, extensive and abundant beds of gypsum, probably developed through evaporation in lagoons and playas, suggest semiaridity. The casts of salt cubes in many localities and at various horizons likewise probably result from dryness. Other evidences, of more doubtful significance, are the lack of soils at any of the depositional "breaks" and the general scarcity of fossil plants of humid-climate type.

PALEOGEOGRAPHY

The form of the Moenkopi depositional basin is illustrated on the isopach map (Fig. 7). It consists, in general, of a wedge of sediments that is thickest to the northwest and thins southeastward toward a vanishing point in western Colorado, eastern Arizona, and western New Mexico. The maximum recorded thickness of the formation is 2150 feet in southwestern Utah, but still greater thicknesses, now eroded, may once have been represented in the Nevada area to the northwest. Furthermore, Lower Triassic deposits in northern Utah and southern Idaho which are 2000 to 3000 feet thick, although designated by different formational names, doubtless originally were continuous with the Moenkopi deposits to the south.

The eastern margin of the depositional basin forms two major embayments separated by a westward-projecting ridge or prong that extends from the vicinity of

---

[5] Fish-eating types (long-snouted gavials) probably indicate perennial rivers or lakes.

Canyon de Chelly toward Tuba City, Arizona. The southern embayment extends eastward beyond Gallup, New Mexico, and marginal deposits, less than 100 feet thick in that area, contain much impure sandstone and relatively little mudstone, indicating proximity to source. The northern embayment extends eastward into Colorado in the area south of Gateway (Dane, 1935, p. 51), where its deposits attain a maximum thickness of over 1000 feet. Throughout this area and adjoining parts of Utah the Moenkopi contains abundant conglomerate, arkose, and gritty material indicating a near-by source, probably the Uncompahgre Upland to the northeast. In the Moenkopi section northeast of Hittel's ranch, Utah, Dane (1935, p. 48) records pebbles up to 1 inch in diameter, and in the section at Dolores River Canyon he describes cobbles 12 to 18 inches in diameter. Rock types in the gravels include schist, pegmatite, gneiss, and graphic granite.

The prong or ridge that extends westward into the Moenkopi basin of northeastern Arizona is shown (1) by the absence of Moenkopi deposits at Nazlini, Canyon de Chelly, Lukachukai, and Carrizo Mountains, in all of which places Shinarump conglomerate rests on Permian beds; and (2) by the relatively thin sections of Moenkopi, with little of the basal member represented, at The Gap, Cedar Ridge, and west of Shadow Mountain. Deposits on the northwest flank of the prong, as at Lees Ferry, Arizona, include an exceptionally low percentage of sand; these deposits are almost entirely mudstone, which fact suggests that the major streams that carried coarser detrital sediments into the embayments were far to the northeast and southeast.

Marine limestones of the Moenkopi formation extend far eastward in the central Utah region, where, during the time represented by the *Meekoceras* zone, they were deposited throughout the San Rafael Swell area and as far east as the Green River (McKnight, 1940, p. 57). Farther south, near the Arizona-Utah line, limestones with *Meekoceras* fauna extend eastward only as far as Kaibab Gulch or about midway across the state (Gregory, 1948, p. 227). Thus, the shoreward margin of marine limestones roughly parallels the boundary of the basin itself, with an embayment to the north and a westward swing farther south. Whether or not the marine limestones once extended eastward into the Arizona embayment cannot be determined because of lack of Triassic outcrops across most of northwestern Arizona.

The former westward extent of the Moenkopi basin has not been definitely determined. Moenkopi-type sediments have been recorded from as far west as the Charleston and Goodsprings Mountains in southern Nevada, and Lower Triassic strata of other types, including much volcanic material, occur in various parts of western Nevada and in the Inyo Mountains, California. Differences in lithologic character indicate that the eastern and western deposits accumulated in separate troughs, but the waters of these geosynclines probably were connected, at least during the time of *Meekoceras*, as indicated by common faunas (Nolan, 1943, p. 158). Thus, a ridge or physical barrier, perhaps submarine in part, probably separated the Moenkopi trough from that of Early Triassic age to the west. Absence of Moenkopi deposits southwest of the thick Charleston Mountain section caused Gregory and Noble (1923, p. 233) to suggest that "a high mountain mass" may have existed in that area; however, the lack of any coarse detrital sediment in the Moenkopi of southern Nevada makes such a conclusion unlikely.

CONDITIONS OF DEPOSITION

Deposition of sediments in the Moenkopi basin was both by marine and by subaerial processes. The formation is the product of a mixture of environments including shallow-sea, delta, lacustrine, playa, flood-plain, and probably various others. Evidence for the origin of some types is definite and easy to recognize; for others it is not clear.

The classification of Moenkopi deposits into basic rock types and the analysis of these, together with their contained structures, have been attempted earlier in this paper. Each of these basic types represents a distinctive environment, and so, through a consideration of their abundance and distribution in different parts of the formation, some idea of the complex mixture of types may be had. Essential to a correct interpretation is the analysis of primary structures and fossils in relation to the rock types containing them.

Stream deposits consisting of coarse silts, sands, and some gravels are abundant along the eastern margins of the depositional basin, and in certain localities they form up to 50 per cent of the section. Some of the stream-formed units are spread for many miles westward into the basin, and a few extend nearly half way across Arizona and Utah. Most of them are cross-stratified on a medium to large scale with types of stratification that result from scour-and-fill or from foreset deposition on delta fronts. They contain abundant cusp ripple marks indicating strong, localized current action, and in a number of localities preserve the skulls and bones of large amphibians. In places they contain mud or clay pellets derived from underlying deposits by the scouring of currents, and, for the most part, they are lenticular and marked by local erosion surfaces.

Along the eastern margin of the Moenkopi basin, mudflat deposits consisting of red, shaly siltstones, many of them ripple-marked, are interspersed between units of stream-deposited sandstone. Farther out in the basin, mudflat deposits constitute a considerable per cent of the entire formation, and in the thick sections of Nevada and western Utah they largely make up the "red members" that separate the limy marine members and the gypsum member. Shrinkage cracks, rain-drop pits, and casts of salt crystals suggest that these shaly siltstones were formed in a subaerial environment. Whether these mudflats that were so widespread during the Lower Triassic epoch were river flood plains or tidal flats or both has not been determined. The red color may favor the flood-plain theory, though possibly the red could have been preserved under tidal waters, especially if salinity were sufficiently high to prevent the activity of sulphate-reducing bacteria. The constant orientation of the ever-present parallel ripple marks is a characteristic of modern tidal flats and favors this mode of origin. Scarcity of vertebrate trackways, common elsewhere in the formation, likewise is believed to be more normal to a tidal-flat environment.

Evidence that wide bodies of quiet water, probably lakes or ponds, formed back from the margins of the sea is found in the deposits of deep red-brown, structureless, crumbly claystone. Especially significant are deposits of this type near Lees Ferry, Arizona, where they constitute a major part of the section, but many thick layers are also present along the Little Colorado Valley and in southeastern Utah, away from the marginal areas. The mud forming these deposits has been accumulated through settling in water so that no bedding or lamination was developed. Abundant shrinkage cracks and reptile tracks have formed on upper surfaces of these deposits as shown by casts in overlying sandstones.

Fresh- or brackish-water ponds in which small bodies of limestone developed occur in a few places in the region of the Little Colorado Valley. The limestones form small, local lenses among red mudstones and claystones. Some of them contain concentrations of a single species of pelecypod; one at Meteor Crater preserved the skulls of many amphibians. These limestones contain varying amounts of clay and silt and, in places, grade into calcareous mudstones.

Lagoons and playas of varying size apparently formed along the margins of and back from the sea as indicated by beds and lentils of gypsum. At some horizons these deposits are remarkably widespread, but most individual beds are thin and local. Evaporation must have been considerable to have formed the large number of these deposits scattered throughout the formation.

Tidal-pool deposits are believed to be represented by "green-gray pyritic carbonaceous shales" of the San Rafael Swell area in Utah (Gilluly and Reeside 1928, p. 65). These gray mudstones are local in distribution and grade laterally into red, shaly mudstones. Although no fossils have been found in them to prove marine origin, the lack of red color and the presence of pyrite are believed evidence of much sulfur accumulation due to organic matter in stagnant ponds. Gray beds similarly replace red ones near the Green River (McKnight, 1940, p. 60), in the correlative Woodside and Thaynes formations on Vermilion Creek, Moffat County, Colorado (Sears, 1925, p. 281, 284), and the south flank of Blue Mountain, Colorado (Spieker and Reeside, in Gilluly and Reeside, 1928, p. 65). In the Green River area, thickness of gray deposits and the large area covered by them convinced McKnight that local tidal pools could not have been the cause there, but that the gray beds may represent marine strata.

Definite marine deposits in the Moenkopi formation are limestones of the Timpoweap, Virgin, and Sinbad members and calcareous shaly mudstones, mostly yellow or gray, interbedded with these limestones. Both types of rock contain marine fossils in many places. All the limestone members thicken westward and northwestward from central Utah, indicating that the axis of the seaway was in that direction. Even in the thickest sections of southwestern Utah, however, the limestone beds do not form a continuous series but are separated by calcareous mudstones. Thus, a considerable amount of detrital sediment was periodically carried far westward into the sea.

The general conclusion regarding conditions of deposition represented by the Moenkopi formation is, as expressed by Baker (1933, p. 36), that a broad plain sloped gently toward the sea to the west and northwest from higher lands in Colorado and New Mexico. Because of extremely low gradient, thin marine limestones were deposited over wide areas to the west, whereas farther east extensive mud flats developed with lakes, playas, and lagoons scattered over their surfaces. From higher areas of the Uncompahgre Upland and the western New Mexico region sands and other detrital sediments were spread by rivers out onto the plain, advancing as delta fronts toward the sea. The geographic positions of various environmental features shifted back and forth during Moenkopi deposition, but, in general, continental deposits progressed westward at the expense of marine areas.

TRANSGRESSION AND REGRESSION

The earliest deposition of Moenkopi sediments probably was in the northern part of the basin—*i.e.*, in the region of central Utah. This is indicated by the stratigraphic position within the formation of the *Meekoceras* zone, which is believed to approximate a time plane. In southwestern Utah, this zone is at the base (Timpoweap member), whereas, in the area of San Rafael Swell, it occurs in the Sinbad limestone above a series of nonfossiliferous, detrital sediments ranging from 100 to 200 feet in thickness.

Initial Moenkopi sedimentation in the east-central Utah region probably resulted from a sinking of the basin with resulting transgression of the sea from the northwest. Marine planation of Permian strata that formed the surface is suggested by the even contact between them and the overlying Lower Triassic strata and by the truncated tops of locally folded beds, according to Dane (1935, p. 52). Coastal-plain peneplanation is given (p. 53) as an alternate explanation. In that area basal Moenkopi deposits are, in part, reworked detrital sediments of Permian age, supplied through the bevelling action of the advancing sea. Gypsum beds that form the base in several localities are attributed to lagoonal development, possibly the result of off-shore bars.

In southwestern Utah where Moenkopi deposition began somewhat later than to the north, limestones containing the *Meekoceras* fauna are near the base. Preceding transgression of the sea in which these were formed, however, stream-cut valleys and canyons of considerable size were carved into the Permian Kaibab limestone, and these canyons in turn were filled with gravels of various sizes, shapes, and compositions. The origin of these gravel deposits is not clear. Some gravels are angular and, judging from their composition, of local derivation; others are well rounded and sorted, showing evidence of much transportation. The matrix of the conglomerate is mostly limestone, and some conglomerate beds are interstratified with limestone beds, a fact suggesting that part at least accumulated on the sea floor. Possibly the gravels were produced by stream action prior to transgression of the sea, but they may have resulted from waves of the advancing marine waters.

A regression of the sea from southwestern Utah is indicated by red shaly siltstones above the Timpoweap. They represent a time of basin filling which forced the sea to retreat. Previously it had reached a maximum advance in which limestone beds were developed as far east as Kaibab Gulch in the south and Green River in the north. After the basin was filled with silt and mud, widespread erosion began, as shown in many places by surface irregularities on the "lower red member" and in some localities by complete removal of earlier Moenkopi sediments.

In southwestern Utah a second transgression of the Lower Triassic sea is represented by the Virgin limestone member. No evidence of this sea has been recognized in the central Utah (San Rafael Swell) area, a fact suggesting that the crustal warping probably responsible for transgression was not uniform over the entire basin of deposition. Along the Arizona-Utah border, however, the belt of limestone accumulation extended east beyond Fredonia, probably to House Rock Valley, at the time of maximum advance.

Duplicating the early Moenkopi history of marine deposition followed by accumulation of continental red silts and clays, the Virgin limestone member was formed and followed by a period of regression. Muds and silts once more filled the basin faster than it sank. These deposits compose the middle red member.

Although in the Moenkopi formation there are few marine limestone beds higher than those of the Virgin to indicate later transgressions of the sea, extensive gypsum accumulations in the Shnabkaib member suggest that for a third time sinking of the basin was more rapid than filling with silt. Thus lagoons or ponds, in which the evaporites were precipitated, were developed over wide areas back from the sea. Finally, however, regression was resumed with sheets of silt and sand advancing westward across the basin to form the upper red member as the final product of Moenkopi deposition.

Moenkopi strata in northeastern Arizona are believed to have formed during the latter part of the formation's history as shown by stratigraphic evidence previously presented. The massive sandstone units were laid down as sheets of river-borne debris carried westward from the margins of the basin. The relative thinness but persistence over wide areas of some of the sandstones, notably the "lower massive" and "upper massive," can best be explained as the effect of very slow sinking of the basin. The result was that stream deposits built forward rather than upward over a long time. Because the base level of deposition was raised so slowly, the delta fronts advanced many miles out into the basin from their sources, and the two main sheets of sandstone may be considered records of regression.

During the westward advance of the "lower massive" sand sheet, an unconformity must have developed above these deposits, or many large diastems developed through them, for deposition was mainly forward and not on top. The magnitude of the break or breaks, furthermore, should be expected to be progressively greater toward the east or place of start in the development of the blanket of sand. Field evidence is not conclusive in this respect, but many examples of erosion surfaces above the massive sandstones have been recorded from the eastern part of the basin. This relationship of the Moenkopi deposits to planes of time, as visualized in the theory of a nearly stable base level, is illustrated in Figure 8.

A

B

Section at Piute Farms, Utah, showing alternation of claystones and mudstones with resistant sandstones. Shinarump conglomerate at
top; Organ Rock member of Cutler formation
below (out of sight).

Valley cut in Kaibab limestone, filled with deposits of Timpoweap member; west of St. George,
Utah. Photo by Poborski.

C

Conglomerate in lower part of Timpoweap member, west of St. George, Utah.
Photo by Poborski.

LITHOLOGIC FEATURES OF MOENKOPI FORMATION

Shnabkaib member (including white gypsum bed) (Sh.) and
middle red member (m.r.) at Vermilion Cliffs, 13 miles west of
Navajo Bridge, Arizona. Navajo sandstone (N.), Jurassic

Upper red member (u.r.) and Shnabkaib member (Sh.) near Fredonia, Arizona. Cap of Shinarump conglomerate (S), Triassic

Middle red member (m.r.), Virgin limestone member (V.), and
lower red member (l.r.) in Frenchman Mountains, Nevada

MEMBERS OF MOENKOPI FORMATION

Bedded gypsum in shaly mudstone, Shnabkaib member, near
Fredonia, Arizona

Cross-laminated, aeolian (?) bed of gypsum in Shnabkaib member, Vermilion Cliffs, 13 miles west of Navajo Bridge, Arizona

Veins of selenite in red Moenkopi mudstone, near Fredonia, Arizona

GYPSUM DEPOSITS

A

Mud and clay balls, base of massive sandstone, Bears Ears, Utah

B

Cusp ripple marks, thick-bedded sandstone of Holbrook member, south of Cameron, Arizona

C

Shrinkage cracks in limestone, Virgin limestone member, west of St. George, Utah. Photo by Poborski.

SEDIMENTARY STRUCTURES

A

Low-angle, simple-type cross-lamination in sandy limestone, Timpoweap member, west of St. George, Utah. Photo by Poborski.

B

Planar-type cross-bedding in lower massive sandstone near Snowflake, Arizona

C

Shallow trough-type cross-lamination, in siltstone near Snowflake, Arizona

CROSS-STRATIFICATION

A. Casts of shrinkage cracks in parallel type ripple marks in shaly siltstone, Wupatki, Arizona.
B. Cross-ripple marks of asymmetrical type, Wupatki, Arizona.
C. Symmetrical ripple marks with small crest in troughs, Wupatki member, S. of Grey Mountain Trading Post, Arizona.
D. Cusp-type ripple marks in thick-bedded sandstone, Holbrook member, Black Point, Arizona.
E. Ripple-lamination in upper red member, Frenchman Mountains, Nevada.

RIPPLE STRUCTURES

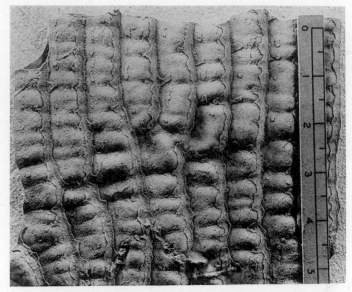

Current ripple marks with wave ripple marks in troughs, natural cast in shaly siltstone, Wupatki member, 20 miles west of Shadow Mountain, Arizona

Current ripple marks with shrinkage cracks superimposed, red siltstone of Holbrook member, 5 miles west of Cameron, Arizona

RIPPLE STRUCTURES

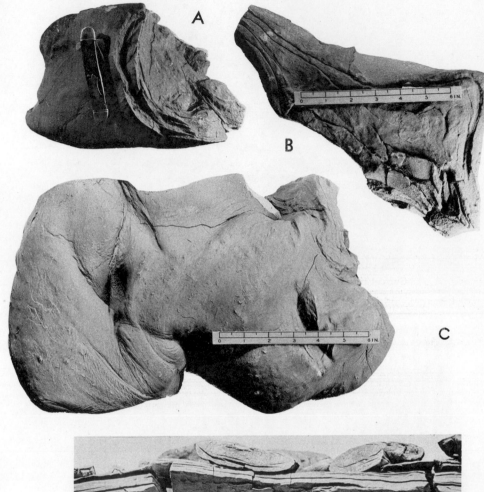

A. Core-and-shell structure from Wupatki member, near Cameron, Arizona.
B. Core-and-shell structure from Holbrook member, near Gap Trading Post, Arizona.
C. Core-and-shell structure from Wupatki member, 2 miles east of Wupatki Ruin, Arizona.
    D. Ripple lamination etched on siltstone surface and layer of core-and-shell structure above, Moqui member, east of Black Point, Arizona.

CORE-AND-SHELL STRUCTURE AND RIPPLE LAMINATION

A

Flow marks in shaly siltstone, Wupatki member, near Winslow,
Arizona

B

Current crescent in shaly siltstone, Holbrook member, north of Cedar
Ridge Trading Post, Arizona

C

Flow marks and plant drags in shaly siltstone, Wupatki member, quarry
east of Flagstaff, Arizona

FLOW MARKS AND CURRENT CRESCENTS

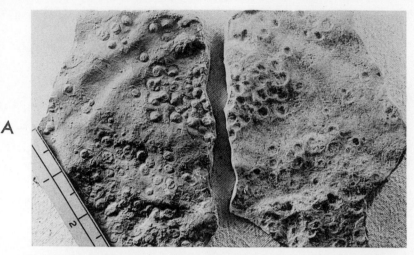

A

Rain pits and casts in shaly siltstone, Wupatki member, 7 miles east of Flagstaff,
Arizona

B

Contorted bedding in Moqui member, east of Black Point, Arizona

C

Casts of salt crystals, shaly siltstone, near base of Wupatki member, 2 miles
south of Cameron, Arizona

RAIN PITS, SALT CASTS, CONTORTED BEDDING

Markings left by swimming animal in shallow water, Wupatki member, quarry east
of Flagstaff, Arizona

Worm trails, Wupatki member, 4 miles southwest of Cameron, Arizona

ANIMAL TRACKS AND TRAILS

A

B

Arthropod track, Wupatki member, quarry
east of Flagstaff, Arizona

Worm borings, Wupatki member, 6 miles south of
Cameron, Arizona

TRAILS OF INVERTEBRATE ANIMALS

DESCRIPTIONS OF SECTIONS

SECTION 1.—*The "Sinks", Snowflake, Arizona*

Measured on escarpment about 2 miles south of the "Sinks" (Dip 4° s.)

Shinarump conglomerate (?):
 Conglomerate: cross-laminated on large scale; beds 5–15 ft. thick; weathers to very large rounded boulders ("rock babies"); develops prominent cliff, forms mesa cap;
 matrix: fine-grained, very pale-brown, slightly calcareous, micaceous sandstone;
 gravel: ¼–½ in., durable rock including jasper, chert, and quartzite;
 contains lenses of weak red, flat-bedded shale.

Moenkopi formation:
Holbrook member:
 1. Claystone: weak reddish brown with yellowish gray patches or bands, sandy, slightly calcareous; contains a few ledges of:
 Siltstone: thin-bedded (4–6 in.), resistant

	Feet
Forms slope	16.5
2. Gypsum: contains mudstone parting in center	3.0
3. Claystone: pale reddish brown, slightly calcareous, brittle; forms slope	5.5
4. Siltstone: pale reddish brown to very pale brown, calcareous, shaly, thin-bedded; conspicuously cross-laminated on medium scale (6–30 in.); with shallow festoon-type laminae throughout; forms slope with weak cliff at top	24.5
5. Gypsum: forms bed	1.5
6. Claystone: yellowish gray to weak reddish brown, slightly calcareous, shaly; contains network of selenite veins cutting through beds; contains ledge of thicker beds in middle; forms slope	15.0
7. Sandstone: very pale brown, very fine-grained, slightly calcareous, friable, locally shaly; forms weak ledge	3.5
8. Gypsum: pure; forms steep slope; alternates with: Claystone: pale reddish brown to very pale brown, slightly calcareous, very thin-bedded; Total	11.5
Total Holbrook member	81.0

Moqui member (?):
 Concealed: flat bench 60.5
Wupatki member (?):

	Feet
9. Claystone: pale reddish brown to weak yellow, calcareous, shaly; contains many current ripple marks; forms slope	6.0
10. Siltstone: pale reddish brown, shaly; forms slope	5.5
11. Siltstone: pale reddish brown, calcareous; weathers rounded; forms massive resistant ledge	5.5
12. Siltstone: pale reddish brown, shaly; partly concealed near center; forms slope	10.0
Total Wupatki member	27.0
Total Moenkopi	168.5

Unconformity: assumed
Kaibab formation:
 Limestone: light yellowish brown, sandy, thick-bedded (2–3 ft.); locally ripple-marked; weathers pale orange, rounded; forms massive ledges or cliff

SECTION 2.—*South of St. Johns, Arizona*

Measured at Roger's Ranch on Little Colorado

Shinarump conglomerate:
 Conglomerate: cross-laminated, massive; abundance of well-rounded gravels, 1–3 in. in diameter; forms cliff

Feet

Unconformity: small erosion channels (2–3 ft.) filled with Shinarump conglomerate

Moenkopi formation:

1. Sandstone: pale yellowish brown, medium-grained, thick-bedded (3–6 ft.); cross-laminated on large scale; massive, friable; contains mud pellets and many kaolin grains; forms cliff; weathers dark yellowish brown.......................... 10.0

2. Mudstone: grayish red, shaly, crumbly; forms slope.......................... 22.0

3. Sandstone: grayish orange, fine-grained; cross-laminated on medium scale throughout; massive; contains small lense of limestone conglomerate with pebbles up to ½ in. in diameter; forms ledges (1–2 ft. thick); weathers moderate brown; contains skull; worm borings and trails on top surface; contains cusp ripple marks and shrinkage cracks.. 8.5

4. Sandstone: grayish orange, fine-grained, massive; lensing character; weathers to brown, rounded cliff... 7.0

5. Claystone: grayish red, brittle, very crumbly; forms slope...................... 8.0

6. Siltstone: yellowish gray, thin-bedded; forms weak ledge; locally contains cusp ripples... 2.0

7. Mudstone: yellowish gray to pale red, crumbly, forms slope.................... 2.5

8. Siltstone: medium gray, thick-bedded (one resistant bed); cross-laminated on medium scale throughout; forms ledge; weathers pale reddish brown.............. 4.0

9. Claystone: white, limy; locally includes irregular fragments of limestone and chert; forms slope... 15.0

10. Conglomerate: forms weak ledge... 2.0
    Matrix: pinkish-gray limestone
    Gravel: angular to subangular blocks and fragments of brown limestone; very poorly sorted

Total Moenkopi.. 81.0

Kaibab limestone: moderate yellowish brown, fine-grained, thick-bedded (1–3 ft.); contains iron concretions; forms ledge; weathers to brown, pitted surface; contains fossil molds.. 11.0
exposed

SECTION (Partial) 3.—*Concho, Arizona*

Measured on west side of Little Colorado Valley about 12 miles west of Concho on Highway 260

Unconformity:
Long slope, largely concealed, with mantle of Upper Triassic gravels. Scattered outcrops indicate presence of Chinle marl.

Moenkopi formation:
Holbrook member:

Feet

1. Sandstone: very light brownish gray, fine- to medium-grained, cross-laminated; weathers rounded; forms massive ledge.................................... 1.0

2. Sandstone: dark reddish gray, very fine-grained, very thin-bedded, crumbly; locally fills deep channel (est. 12 ft.) in underlying bed; forms slope............ 4.5

3. Sandstone: light olive gray, fine- to medium-grained, slightly calcareous, cross-laminated on medium scale; locally contains subangular to rounded gravels of siltstone and limestone averaging ½ in.; weathers buff; forms ledge (mesa rim).. 1.0

4. Sandstone: light olive gray grading upward to weak red, fine-grained, friable, cross-laminated (laminae ¼–½ in.); contains ripple marks; weathers light brownish gray; forms slope.. 12.0

5. Conglomerate: irregularly bedded; weathers red brown; contains vertebrate skulls, interclavicles, jaw... 4.5
    matrix: light olive-gray, calcareous siltstone;
    gravel: subangular to rounded pebbles, mostly ¼ in. or less, rarely ½ in., of light-gray and light olive-gray, argillaceous limestone.

6. Mudstone: pale reddish brown and light olive gray, very calcareous, structureless;

Feet

rests on top of light-gray massive sandstones in places, elsewhere on top of mudstones and sandstones of channel fill; forms slope........................... 21.0

Total Holbrook member.. **44.0**
Undifferentiated members:
7. Sandstone: light olive gray, cross-laminated; like basal part of no. 9.............0–11.0

8. Sandstone: light gray, fine- to very fine-grained, very calcareous, cross-laminated;
beds medium in thickness ($\frac{1}{2}$–2 ft.); alternates with:
Mudstone: weak red and light olive gray, structureless, brittle;
Beds slope from margin of channel toward center, forming channel fill and 3$\frac{1}{2}$-ft.
covering of hill.. 20.5

9. Sandstone: light olive gray to pale red, very fine-grained and silty near base, calcareous; cross-laminated on large scale showing prominent scour and fill structure; weathers pale reddish brown, massive; grades up into:
Sandstone: light gray to pale red, medium-grained; contains mud pellets and gravels
(gravels average $\frac{1}{4}$ in. subangular, limestone and siltstone with subordinate
flint and quartz); weathers rounded; forms massive cliff..................12.5–29.5

10. Mudstone: weak reddish brown with light olive-gray bands, calcareous, structureless, crumbly; forms slope....................................exposed   9.0

Total undifferentiated members..................................... **70.0**
Total Moenkopi measured.. **114.0**
Base concealed by alluvium of valley fill

SECTION 4.—*Woodruff Butte, Arizona*

Measured at west base of butte, 8 miles east of Holbrook

(Dip 14° southeast where measured)

Chinle formation:
Claystone: dark reddish gray, structureless, crumbly; contains lenses of light-gray
sandstone; weathers to prominent light-gray band at base; gray marls above
Unconformity: No Shinarump conglomerate represented

Moenkopi formation:
Holbrook member:

Feet

1. Much concealed: slope; at top contains:
Claystone: dusky red and light olive gray, crumbly
Total... 22.5

2. Siltstone: weak reddish brown and light olive gray, shaly, crumbly; much con-
cealed; alternates with:
Siltstone: pale brown, flat-bedded, fissile; forms thin ledges
Forms slope... 5.5

3. Sandstone: light brownish gray, very fine-grained, thin-bedded (2–6 in.); partly
concealed; forms ledge... 5.5

4. Conglomerate:.. 0.5
matrix: light olive gray silty limestone;
gravel: white and light olive-gray limestone pebbles, mostly under $\frac{1}{4}$ in. diameter (max. $\frac{1}{2}$ in.), angular to subrounded.

5. Sandstone: light brownish gray, very fine-grained; like no. 3; cross-laminated on
small scale; forms ledge... 0.5

6. Conglomerate: light olive gray; like no. 4............................ 2.5

7. Lower 30 ft. concealed; above 30 ft.:
Mudstone: light olive gray and weak reddish brown; like no. 2
Total... 43.0

8. Sandstone; dusky red, fine-grained, calcareous, crumbly; cross-laminated on large
scale; forms slope.. 4.5

9. Siltstone: weak red, sandy, calcareous, irregularly bedded; forms slope, much concealed; alternates with:

Feet

Sandstone: very light olive gray to weak red, fine-grained to silty, calcareous; contains bone fragments; weathers light olive gray; forms thin ledges (1–3 in.) . . . . .
Total 9.0

10. Sandstone: very light brownish gray to pale red, fine-grained to silty (contains some medium grains scattered throughout); calcareous, locally micaceous; cross-laminated on large scale; basal 2 ft. contains white and light olive gray limestone pebbles up to ¼ in. diameter; locally forms "rock babies" 43.0

11. Mudstone: weak reddish brown, crumbly; like no. 2; contains:
Siltstone: light brownish gray, calcareous, crumbly
Forms slope 10.0

12. Sandstone: light brownish gray, fine-grained to silty; like no. 10; forms "rock babies" 6.0

13. Claystone: dark reddish gray, silty, brittle; like no. 2; forms slope 9.0

14. Sandstone: pale red to light olive gray; like no. 10; weathers locally to rounded "rock babies", elsewhere to flat, thin lamination surfaces; forms weak cliff 22.0

15. Mudstone: weak reddish brown, structureless; like no. 2; forms slope 5.0

16. Sandstone: light brown to light brownish gray, fine-grained, calcareous, **friable**; cross-laminated on large scale; weathers weak reddish brown; forms ledge 8.0

Total Holbrook member 196.5

Moqui member:
17. Concealed Upper 45.5 ft. probably Moqui member 95.5
Lower 50 ft. probably Wupatki member
Wupatki member:

18. Sandstone: pale red, very fine-grained, calcareous, friable; cross-laminated **on** medium scale; weathers weak reddish brown, massive, locally with honey-comb structure; forms cliff 11.0

19. Mudstone: pale reddish brown, calcareous, shaly; alternates with:
Mudstone: dusky red, brittle; like no. 2
Forms slope 9.0

20. Mudstone: light yellowish brown, calcareous shaly (fissile toward top), ripple-marked; forms slope 5.5

Total Wupatki member 25.5
Total Moenkopi 317.5

Unconformity: erosion to a flat surface, with local irregularities of steplike character where beds rise above surface
Coconino sandstone:
Sandstone: pale yellow with light to dark yellowish brown spots, fine-grained, friable; cross-laminated

Section 5.—*Winslow, Arizona*

Composite section: top to bed 7 measured 2 miles northwest of Moqui station; beds 8–20 along Moqui Wash south of Highway 66 (by Frank Peabody); bed 21 to base in canyon 2.3 miles south of Winslow, along telephone line.
Shinarump conglomerate:
Sandstone: very pale brown; contains scattered gravel; cross-laminated throughout; massive
Unconformity: surface of relief up to 2 ft.

Moenkopi formation:
Holbrook member:

Feet

1. Mudstone: weak brown and light olive gray, crumbly, brittle; forms slope 20.0

2. Sandstone: weak reddish brown, very fine-grained, calcareous, fissile; forms series of ledges; alternates with thin beds of:
Mudstone: light brown and very light olive gray, calcareous; forms slopes
Total 15.5

3. Mudstone: light brown and very light olive gray; forms partly concealed slopes; alternates with a few beds of:
Sandstone: weak reddish brown, very fine-grained, ledge-forming;
Total like no. 2 but with less sandstone.................................... 33.0

4. Sandstone: light brown, fine- to very fine-grained, calcareous, friable; cross-laminated on large scale; contains mud-ball impressions; weathers same color, massive; forms "rock babies".. 22.0

5. Conglomerate: beds ½–3 in. thick; cross-laminated on medium scale; weathers very pale reddish brown.. 0.5
matrix: light olive-gray, fine-grained, calcareous sandstone;
gravels: irregular limestone pebbles up to ¼ in. in diameter.

6. Mudstone: weak reddish brown and very light olive gray, slope-forming; like no. 1; includes two ledges of:
Sandstone: light olive gray, very fine-grained, resistant; beds ½–3 in. thick; contains ripple marks
Total.............. 9.0

7. Sandstone: light olive gray, fine- to very fine-grained, friable, calcareous; cross-laminated on medium scale; weathers pale reddish brown; and:
Conglomerate: very light olive gray; like no. 5
Total forms ledge; lenses out laterally...................................... 7.5
Concealed area: beds 7 and 8 may correspond.

8. Sandstone: pale brown, coarse-grained, calcareous, hard; contains much fresh biotite at base; contains light olive-gray conglomerate (similar to Holbrook conglomerate bone beds); weathers same to weak reddish brown.............. 7.0

Total Holbrook member... 114.5

Moqui member:
9. Mudstone: weak red, calcareous; contains gypsum nodules; forms slope; alternates with:
Siltstone: light yellowish brown to weak reddish brown, slope-forming; like no. 1; occurs as lenses
Total contains much gypsum.. 22.0

10. Siltstone: reddish gray, sandy, cross-laminated, locally ripple-marked; weathers weak reddish brown; forms ledge of platy, irregular, thin slabs................ 6.0

11. Mudstone: dusky red to weak reddish brown; and:
Siltstone: light yellowish brown, calcareous
Total forms much-concealed slope... 27.0

Total Moqui member... 55.0
Wupatki member:

12. Sandstone: reddish gray to dark reddish gray, fine-grained; cross-laminated on large scale; contains mudball casts; contains lenses of conglomerate with bone fragments; contains petrified wood and coprolites; weathers weak reddish brown; forms ledge of thin, irregular slabs; thins toward north...................... 6.0

13. Mudstone: weak red, slope-forming; like no. 1; contains gypsum beds; much concealed.. 8.0

14. Siltstone: weak red, calcareous, thin-bedded; contains *Capitosaur* skull and tracks and *Chirotherium* tracks; forms weak ledge................................. 2.0

15. Claystone: weak reddish brown, weak yellow, and yellowish gray; fissile; forms slope.. 3.0

16. Siltstone: pale brown, calcareous, thin-bedded (½–3 in.), ripple-marked; weathers weak to pale red; horizon of *Capitosaur* skulls and skeleton; forms ledge........ 0.5

17. Mudstone: weak red, slope-forming; like no. 1; much concealed................. 6.0

18. Siltstone: very pale brown; like 16 but more argillaceous; weathers blocky; forms ledge... 1.0

19. Mudstone: weak yellow and weak red, calcareous, shaly; weathers light brown to weak red; alternates with:
Siltstone: weak red, platy; like no. 10
Total.. 27.0

Feet

20. Siltstone: weak red, platy; like no. 10; contains occasional thin conglomerate lenses; forms ledge.. 10.5

21. Siltstone: weak red, calcareous; like no. 20 but not in thin beds; cross-laminated on large scale; weathers same color, massive, locally honey-combed; forms rounded cliff.. 14.0

22. Siltstone: weak yellow to light brown, shaly, calcareous; forms slope............. 2.5

Total Wupatki member... 80.5
Total Moenkopi.. 250.0

Unconformity: contact concealed
Kaibab formation:
  Limestone: light yellowish brown, sandy, aphanitic; grades down into very sandy limestone; weathers same color to moderate brown, rough..................... 5.5
Unconformity: irregular surface with small channels (up to 3 ft.) where examined.
Coconino sandstone:
  Sandstone: very light brown, fine-grained, friable, cross-laminated

SECTION (Partial) 6.—*Meteor Crater, Arizona*

Beds 1–5 measured at quarry near crater, lower beds along Highway 66 north of Meteor Crater (Dip 3° north)

Top of hill: recent erosion surface

Moenkopi formation:
  Wupatki member:

Feet

1. Siltstone: weak red, very calcareous, thin-bedded (1–4 in.), resistant; contains cusp ripple marks; forms ledge 2.0

2. Claystone: weak reddish brown, very calcareous, shaly; forms slope.............. 7.0

3. Claystone: reddish gray, very calcareous, shaly, crumbly; contains fish remains; forms slope.. 1.0

4. Limestone: light brownish gray to dusky red, very silty; contains mud pellet casts, shrinkage cracks, and limestone pebbles on upper surface; contains amphibian skulls and bones (Meteor Crater quarry); weathers reddish brown; forms ledge.. 1.0

5. Mudstone: weak red, calcareous, shaly; contains *Chirotherium* tracks; forms slope; exposed 7.0
Concealed: long slope...estimated 50.0±

6. Siltstone: weak reddish brown to very pale reddish brown, argillaceous, calcareous, shaly; locally cross-laminated on medium scale; locally contains ripple marks; forms slope.. 2.0

7. Sandstone: very pale reddish brown, very fine-grained to silty (well sorted), very calcareous; weakly cross-laminated; beds 1–3 ft. thick; contains cusp ripple marks on upper surface; weathers to honeycomb surface; forms massive rounded ledges (marker bed)... 10.5

8. Concealed.. 6.0

9. Conglomerate..exposed 1.0
matrix: light-brown, medium- to coarse-grained, quartz sandstone with calcareous cement;
gravels: very pale-brown limestone fragments mostly ¼ in. or less, maximum ½ in.

Total Moenkopi measured... 87.5

Unconformity: assumed
Kaibab formation:
  Siltstone: light yellow, argillaceous, calcareous, thin-bedded; weathers rough.

SECTION (Partial) 7.—*Leupp, Arizona*

Measured 3 miles west of Little Colorado River

Recent erosion surface

Feet

Moenkopi formation:
Wupatki member:
1. Sandstone: reddish gray, fine-grained, silty; cross-laminated on large scale (scour-and-fill type); locally splits along laminae into thin, flat sheets; forms massive cliff (locally slope); less resistant than underlying bed...................... 19.0

2. Siltstone: very pale reddish brown speckled with moderate brown, calcareous; weakly cross-laminated on medium scale (1–3 ft.); weathers weak reddish brown, locally with honeycomb surface; forms massive cliff (marker bed).............. 11.0

3. Siltstone: pale reddish brown, calcareous, shaly; locally ripple-marked; 7 ft. above base contains thin (1½ in.) resistant bed of:
Conglomerate:
matrix: light yellowish-brown limestone;
gravels: ¼ in. or less, a few up to ½ in., very pale-brown and very light yellowish-brown silty limestone, and occasional pale-red and white quartz fragments
Total... 16.5

Total Moenkopi measured... 46.5

Unconformity: assumed
Kaibab formation, Alpha member:
Limestone: very pale brown, magnesian, argillaceous; weathers rough, pitted

SECTION (Partial) 8.—*Grand Falls, Arizona*

Measured 3 miles south of the falls

Recent erosion surface

Moenkopi formation:
Wupatki member:

Feet

1. Siltstone: pale red speckled with light brown, calcareous; weathers with honey-comb surface; forms massive ledge (marker bed) capping mesa............... 11.0

2. Siltstone: weak red, shaly; grades to coarse clay; very calcareous; locally shows current ripple marks; forms slope...................................... 10.0

3. Sandstone: weak reddish brown, coarse-grained with silty limestone matrix; grains subangular to rounded, composed of pale reddish-brown, light-gray, and brownish-gray quartz; cross-laminated on small scale; contains pellets of pale to light-brown siltstone, and scattered gravels up to ½ in. diameter; forms resistant ledge.. 2.5

4. Concealed: slope.. 16.5

5. Conglomerate: weathers pitted, moderately resistant.........................3.0–8.0
matrix: light-brown, very calcareous siltstone;
gravel: very pale-brown Kaibab limestone pebbles ½ in. and less in diameter, locally larger in basal 5 ft.

Total measured... 48.0
Unconformity: assumed
Kaibab formation

SECTION (Partial) 9.—*Near Heiser Spring, Arizona*

Measured 2½ miles east of Wupatki Ruin

Top of hill: recent erosion surface

Moenkopi formation:
Wupatki member:

Feet

1. Siltstone: pale reddish brown, calcareous, argillaceous; cross-laminated on small scale; weathers pale brown, pitted surface; forms massive cliff............... 7.0

2. Siltstone: light yellowish brown speckled with light brown, argillaceous, flat-bedded, friable; locally forms cliff with overlying beds...................... 2.0

3. Mudstone: light brown, calcareous, very crumbly, forms recess................. 0.5

Feet

4. Mudstone: pale reddish brown, calcareous, argillaceous, thin-, flat-bedded; forms weak ledge.. 1.0

5. Concealed slope; like no. 6; contains:
Siltstone: very pale orange, calcareous, shaly, weathers with red stain............ 22.0

6. Siltstone: very pale brown, calcareous, argillaceous, thin-bedded (1–3 in.); resistant ledge; contains abundant ripple marks (cusp and parallel), shrinkage cracks; top bed formed of mud curls....................................... 6.5

7. Claystone: pale reddish brown, argillaceous, very weak and crumbly; forms slope, basal portion concealed.. 33.0

Total Moenkopi measured.. 72.0

Unconformity: not apparent; Kaibab surface flat
Kaibab formation:
    Limestone: light yellowish brown, hard, silty; beds (6–12 in.); weathers with pitted surface; contains geodes

SECTION (Partial) 10.—*Wupatki Ruin, Arizona*

Measured ½ mile north of Wupatki Ruin

Top of mesa: recent erosion surface
Moenkopi formation:
  Wupatki member:

Feet

1. Siltstone: pale reddish brown, calcareous, argillaceous, thin-bedded, shaly; forms slope or bench... Trace

2. Siltstone: pale reddish brown, calcareous, argillaceous, very resistant; cross-lamination on small scale throughout; weathers to light-brown, pitted surface; forms massive cliff... 6.5
(at Wupatki Ruin, ½ mi. s., this unit is 16.5 ft. thick)

3. Concealed: slope; upper part contains:
Siltstone: pale reddish brown, calcareous, weak.............................. 7.5

4. Siltstone: pale reddish brown, calcareous, argillaceous, resistant; thin, flat beds with festoon cross-lamination; weathers light brown with pitted surface; forms vertical ledge.. 3.0
(at Wupatki Ruin, ½ mi. s., this unit is 15.0 ft. thick)

5. Claystone: weak red; like bed no. 7, largely concealed, slope................... 25.0

6. Siltstone: weak reddish brown, calcareous, shaly; contains salt molds, parallel ripple marks, shrinkage cracks; forms weak ledge.......................... 2.0

7. Mudstone: weak red to pale reddish brown, crumbly; forms slope largely concealed by talus; contains:
Siltstone: light brown, resistant; forms a few thin ledges (2 in. thick); weathers pale reddish brown
Total.. 29.5

8. Sandstone: very light orange, very fine-grained, calcareous; thin, resistant beds (1–3 in. thick); weathers light yellowish brown, topmost bed contains mud pellets and rounded limestone pebbles in a limy matrix........................ 1.0

9. Mudstone: weak red, argillaceous, crumbly; forms slope...................... 3.0

Total Moenkopi measured.. 77.5

Unconformity: not apparent; surface even, where exposed
Kaibab formation:
    Limestone: light yellowish brown, argillaceous; weathers to rough silty surface; massive beds; contains molds of mollusks................................exp. 3.0

SECTION (Partial) 11.—*North of Wupatki Ruin, Arizona*

Measured 1 mile north of Wupatki Ruin

Top of hill: recent erosion surface
Moenkopi formation:
  Wupatki member:

Feet

1. Siltstone: light red brown, shaly; forms slope.................................... Trace
2. Siltstone: pale reddish brown, argillaceous; forms massive cliff.................. 28.5
3. Siltstone: pale reddish brown, weak; contains worms trails; forms undercut but locally continuous with cliff above.. 2.5
4. Siltstone: pale reddish brown; flat- and ripple-laminated beds; forms receding ledges.. 3.0
5. Siltstone: pale reddish brown; like no. 4 except more resistant.................. 3.0
6. Concealed: slope; 1 ft. above base contains:
Siltstone: pale reddish brown, resistant bed (8 in. thick); contains ripple marks;
Total... 24.0
7. Siltstone: pale reddish brown, shaly; forms weak ledge......................... 1.0
Concealed: slope... 26.5
8. Sandstone: very pale orange; no conglomerate noted; forms ledge............... 1.0
9. Talus: slope.. 1.0

Total Moenkopi measured.. 90.5

Unconformity: not apparent; surface even, where exposed
Kaibab formation:
Limestone: light yellowish brown, argillaceous, weathers to rough silty surface; massive beds; contains molds of mollusks.....................................exp. 3.0

Section (Partial) 12.—East of Black Point, Arizona

Beds 1–9 measured in canyon east of Black Point Little Colorado Valley; bed 9 to base measured on west side of Crack-in-the-Rock

(Beds dipping 10° where measured)

Top of section cut by faulting

Moenkopi formation:
Moqui member: units forming light olive-gray slopes with ledges.

Feet

1. Siltstone: pale brown, sandy, calcareous, very friable; contains ripple laminae throughout; weathers pale reddish brown; forms ledge....................... 4.5
2. Mudstone: weak reddish brown, friable, structureless; contains a few thin beds of very light-gray, fissile mudstone; forms slope............................... 22.5
3. Siltstone: light olive gray, calcareous, micaceous, cross-laminated; contains abundant ripple marks, cores-and-shells of mud; weathers light brown; forms ledge... 1.5
4. Mudstone: light olive gray, calcareous, micaceous, fissile; weathers light brown; forms slope; partly concealed... 14.5
5. Sandstone: very light brown, very fine-grained, calcareous, structureless; beds ½– 1 ft. thick; contains fucoids; weathers weak reddish brown; forms resistant ledge.. 2.0
6. Mudstone: light olive gray; alternates with:
Claystone: weak reddish brown; calcareous, irregularly bedded, friable, weak; total forms slope; partly concealed.................................... 14.5
7. Mudstone: weak red, calcareous, thick-bedded (1–3 ft.); ripple-laminated locally; shows mud-pellet impressions; weathers weak reddish brown; forms massive ledge... 7.5
8. Claystone: weak reddish brown, silty, shaly; alternates with:
Limestone: pale brown, silty, flat-bedded; locally ripple-laminated; weathers pale reddish brown; forms ledge
Total forms slope with ledges... 61.0

Total Moqui member... 128.0

Wupatki member: units forming lower reddish brown slopes and ledges
9. Siltstone: very pale reddish brown speckled with moderate brown, calcareous; locally cross-laminated on large scale; weathers weak reddish brown; forms conspicuous massive cliff (prominent marker bed)............................... 36.5

Feet

10. Siltstone: weak reddish brown, calcareous, thin-bedded, crumbly; contains rain pits; forms slope. 7.5

11. Siltstone: very pale brown to weak reddish brown, calcareous; beds thick (2–12 in.); contains ripple marks; weathers into large blocky slabs; forms very resistant ledge. 4.0

12. Limestone: very pale brown, finely crystalline, silty, thin-bedded (¼–½ in.); ripple-laminated; forms resistant ledges; alternates with:
    Claystone: weak reddish brown, calcareous, thin-bedded; and
    Siltstone: very light olive gray, calcareous, thin-bedded
    Total forms slope with ledges. 27.0

13. Siltstone: weak red, very calcareous, argillaceous, hard; beds thin (¼–1 in.), flat; forms ledge. 2.0

14. Mudstone: weak red, calcareous, shaly, thin-bedded (¼–¾ in.); contains some thicker beds (2–3 in.) of:
    Siltstone: weak red, very calcareous, micaceous; forms ledge 16.5 ft. from base;
    Total weathers weak reddish brown; forms slope. 35.5

15. Conglomerate: beds thin and flat; locally ripple-marked; weathers weak reddish brown; forms ledge. 2.0
    matrix: weak red, calcareous, hard siltstone;
    gravel: angular fragments, mostly less than ¼ in., rarely to ¾ in., mostly very pale-brown chert.

16. Concealed: slope. 5.5

17. Conglomerate. 1.5
    matrix: very pale reddish brown, calcareous sandstone;
    gravels: angular pebbles up to ½ in. diameter of chert, chalcedony, and gray magnesian limestone; very poorly sorted.

Total Wupatki member. 121.5
Total Moenkopi measured. . . . . 249.5+

Unconformity
Kaibab formation:
  Limestone: pale red, aphanitic, silty, massive, resistant; contains *Productus bassi*

SECTION (Partial) 13.—*Black Falls, Arizona*
Measured on east side of Little Colorado River at Inscription Mesa

Shinarump conglomerate:
  Conglomerate: layers of small gravel in light-brown sandstone to base; cross-laminated; weathers brown
Unconformity: surface fairly regular where examined

Moenkopi formation:
  Holbrook member:

Feet

1. Claystone: weak red, silty, structureless, hard; contains thin yellowish-gray bands; weathers rounded; forms slope. 3.0

2. Mudstone: mostly weak to pale reddish brown (predominantly light brown between 55 and 72.5 ft. from base), calcareous, crumbly, brittle; includes ledges of light olive-gray siltstone; forms slope. 86.0

3. Sandstone: light olive gray, very fine-grained, silty, calcareous, resistant, cross-laminated; weathers very light brown to pale reddish brown; forms cliff. 6.0

4. Conglomerate: contains vertebrate tooth, plant stems; weathers light brown; forms ledge. 0.5
   matrix: light olive-gray, very fine-grained, calcareous siltstone;
   gravels: irregular limestone pebbles averaging ¼ in. diameter, up to ½ in.

5. Claystone: very light brown and weak reddish brown, structureless, crumbly, brittle; grades down into:
   Mudstone: light olive gray, shaly; total forms slope; contains ledges of:
   Siltstone: very light olive gray, sandy, calcareous, shaly
   Total. 22.0

Feet

6. Siltstone: very pale brown, very sandy, calcareous; cross-laminated on small scale; weathers very pale reddish brown; forms ledge............................ 3.0

7. Claystone and mudstone: slope-forming; and siltstone: ledge-forming; alternating series like no. 5... 11.0

8. Limestone: light brownish gray to weak red, very silty, hard, cross-laminated; contains weak reddish brown silt pellets in upper part; weathers light brownish gray to weak reddish brown; forms "rock babies"; forms massive ledge (marker bed) capping mesas.......................... 5.5

Total Holbrook member... 137.0

Moqui member:
9. Claystone and mudstone: slope-forming; and siltstone: ledge-forming; alternating series like no. 5... 4.0

10. Sandstone: light olive gray, very fine-grained, ledge-forming; like no. 3; shows ripple lamination................................... 2.0

11. Claystone and mudstone: slope-forming; and siltstone: ledge-forming; alternating series like no. 5... 16.5

12. Sandstone: light olive gray, very fine-grained, ledge-forming; like no. 3.......... 1.5

13. Claystone: weak reddish brown (locally olive gray from deoxidation), structureless, crumbly; forms slope.. 9.5

14. Sandstone: light brownish gray, fine-grained, calcareous, very friable; cross-laminated; weathers pale reddish brown; forms cliff........................... 2.0

15. Claystone and mudstone: slope-forming; and siltstone: ledge-forming; alternating series like no. 5 .... 11.0

16. Sandstone: very light brown, fine- to very fine-grained, argillaceous, calcareous, friable; prominently cross-laminated on medium scale; weathers same color to very pale reddish brown; forms cliff........................... 7.5

Total Moqui member... 54.0
Total Moenkopi measured....................................... 190.5

Base concealed under alluvium

Section (Partial) 14.—*Black Falls, Arizona*

Measured on west side of Little Colorado River (northeast corner Sec. 34, T. 26 N., R. 10 E.)
Top of mesa: recent erosion surface

Moenkopi formation:
Holbrook member:

Feet

1. Siltstone: pale reddish brown, calcareous, cross-laminated; weathers same color; forms resistant ledge..................................exposed 6.0

2. Mudstone: weak red and light olive gray, brittle, crumbly; contains one thin ledge of shaly siltstone; forms slope............................... 20.0

3. Siltstone: light brown to light olive gray, calcareous, prominently cross-laminated; weathers very light brown; forms ledge (rim of mesa); prominent marker bed ("rock baby" horizon?)............................... 3.5

Total Holbrook member............................... 29.5

Moqui member:
4. Mudstone: weak red and light olive gray, calcareous, shaly, locally fissile; alternates with:
Claystone: weak reddish brown, structureless; weathers rounded
Total forms slope.. 19.5

5. Siltstone: very light brownish gray, fissile, calcareous; weathers same color; forms ledge... 1.5

6. Siltstone: weak reddish brown, calcareous, very fissile; forms slope.............. 2.0

7. Sandstone: very light olive gray and light brown, very fine-grained, calcareous, friable, thinly laminated; cut with selenite............................... 3.0

Feet

8. Claystone: weak reddish brown and dark reddish gray; beds 6–30 in. thick; alternates with:
Mudstone: light brown and light olive gray, shaly; beds 2–12 in. thick; some beds contain ripple marks;
Total like no. 4; contains selenite veins throughout............................ 37.0

9. Claystone and mudstone: alternating series like no. 4; contains many gypsum nodules ¼–1 in. in diameter and selenite veins; contains several gypsum beds up to 1 ft. thick, interbedded with light olive-gray shale..................... 23.0

10. Siltstone: weak reddish brown, calcareous, crumbly, fissile; contains some selenite veins; weathers pale reddish brown; forms resistant cliff..................... 9.5

11. Claystone and mudstone: alternating series like no. 4; most beds contain gypsum nodules and selenite veins like no. 9; includes 3-inch bed of gypsum 17.5 ft. above base; total forms cliff.. 23.5

12. Mudstone: weak red, calcareous, structureless; locally deoxidized to light olive gray; contains selenite veins; weathers same color to very pale reddish brown, massive; forms ledge... 6.0

13. Claystone and mudstone: alternating series like no. 4; contains gypsum nodules and selenite veins like no. 9.. 8.5
                                                                              ———
Total Moqui member.. 133.5
Total Moenkopi measured... 163.0
Base concealed: Little Colorado River

SECTION 15.—*West of Black Point, Arizona*

(Strata dipping 26° north where measured)

Shinarump conglomerate:
Sandstone: gray, medium- to coarse-grained, cross-laminated; contains abundance of gravels throughout; weathers massive; forms cliff
Unconformity: assumed
Moenkopi formation:
Holbrook member: units forming upper series of weak reddish-brown ledges and slopes

Feet

1. Concealed: slope... 15.0

2. Sandstone: pale red, very fine-grained, calcareous; cross-laminated on medium scale; weathers weak reddish brown; forms cliff............................ 3.0

3. Claystone: weak red, brittle, crumbly; forms partly concealed slope; alternates with:
Siltstone: weak reddish brown, sandy, thin-bedded, ripple-marked; forms several ledges ½–2 ft. thick
Total... 26.0

4. Sandstone: pale red, fine- to very fine-grained, ledge-forming; like no. 2.......... 2.0

5. Claystone: weak reddish brown and yellowish brown; and siltstone: weak reddish brown; alternating series like no. 3.................................... 28.0

6. Sandstone: pale red, very fine-grained, ledge-forming; like no. 2................. 1.5

7. Claystone: weak red; forms slopes; contains thin ledges of:
Siltstone: yellowish gray and pale reddish brown, calcareous, friable
Total... 5.0

8. Sandstone: pale red, very fine-grained, cliff-forming; like no. 2; contains mudballs and ripple marks; contains *Chirotherium* tracks (large and small types) and large plant stems; contains lenses of:
Conglomerate: light olive gray (bone conglomerate); weathers weak reddish brown; matrix: light olive-gray, calcareous siltstone;
gravels: rounded limestone pebbles less than ¼ in. diameter;
Total forms cliff...3.0–6.0

9. Concealed: slope.. 7.5

10. Siltstone: weak reddish brown, very sandy, micaceous, calcareous; cross-laminated on large scale; beds thick (2–6 ft.); weathers same color, massive, rounded; forms cliff ("rock-baby" horizon?).. 15.0
                                                                              ———
Total Holbrook member... 118.0

Feet

Moqui member: units forming very pale reddish brown and light olive gray slope.
11. Claystone: weak reddish brown to light olive gray, silty, calcareous, crumbly, very brittle; forms slopes 10–20 ft. thick; alternates with:
Siltstone: light olive gray, sandy, shaly, ripple-marked; forms ledges ½–2 ft. thick
Total forms slope which weathers with very pale reddish-brown and light olive-gray bands; contains gypsum.. 144.0
Wupatki member: units forming lower series of weak reddish brown ledges and slopes

12. Siltstone: weak reddish brown, argillaceous, calcareous; cross-laminated on medium scale; weathers same color; forms cap of mesas............................ 2.5

13. Siltstone: light brown, ripple-marked, ledge-forming; like no. 12; alternates with:
Mudstone: weak reddish brown, crumbly; forms slopes;
Total.. 9.0

14. Concealed: slope.. 9.0

15. Siltstone: weak reddish brown, ripple-marked, ledge-forming; like no. 12 but thin-bedded (¼–½ in.).. 2.5

16. Sandstone: very pale reddish brown speckled with moderate brown, very fine-grained, calcareous; cross-laminated on large scale; weathers weak reddish brown, massive, locally honeycombed; forms prominent cliff........................ 12.5

17. Siltstone: weak reddish brown and yellowish gray, calcareous, shaly, crumbly; forms slope; alternates with:
Siltstone: weak red, argillaceous, ripple-laminated; beds 1–2 ft. thick; weathers weak reddish brown; forms ledges;
Total.. 23.5

18. Siltstone: weak red; like ledge-forming siltstone in no. 17................... 3.5

19. Siltstone: very light brown and weak reddish brown, shaly, slope forming; grades up into no. 18.. 6.5

20. Siltstone: weak red; like ledge-forming siltstone in no. 17................... 3.0

21. Claystone: weak reddish brown, calcareous, crumbly, silty, shaly; alternates with:
Claystone: weak reddish brown, structureless; weathers rounded;
Total forms slope... 13.5

22. Siltstone: weak red, argillaceous; beds 2–18 in. thick; contains many ripple marks; weathers weak reddish brown; forms weak ledge........................... 3.0

23. Claystone: weak reddish brown, shaly and structureless, slope forming; like no. 21... 13.5

Total Wupatki member... 102.0
Total Moenkopi... 364.0

Unconformity: surface determined by Kaibab beds, some of which rise in steps above general level; no conglomerate at section
Kaibab limestone:
Limestone: pale red, aphanitic; weathers very pale brown; forms resistant thick ledges (6–12 inches thick)

SECTION (Partial) 16.—*Cameron, Arizona*

Measured ¼ mile west of Highway 89, 6 miles south of Cameron, on old Cameron highway.

(Dip 10° north where beds 1–12 were measured, 2° north below bed 12)

Shinarump conglomerate:
Conglomerate: white to brown, prominently cross-laminated nearly to base; forms massive cliff; gravels: angular to subangular, mostly ½ in. or less.
Unconformity: erosion channel cut down to bed 7 (38 ft.) within distance of ¼ mile, filled with Shinarump conglomerate.

Moenkopi formation:
Holbrook member; units forming upper series of weak reddish-brown ledges and slopes:

Feet

1. Claystone: weak reddish brown, brittle, structureless or weakly cross-laminated; weathers with knobby surface; forms recess............................... 2.0–3.0

2. Siltstone: purplish, shaly; forms slope.................................... 7.0

Feet

3. Siltstone: weak red; contains amphibian skull (fauna M) and poorly preserved pelecypods (fauna N); prominently cross-laminated on medium scale; forms rounded ledge with bench above... 4.5

4. Claystone: weak reddish brown, calcareous, brittle; contains bed of fissile weak red siltstone; forms slope.. 15.0

5. Siltstone: weak reddish brown, cross-laminated (laminae 1–3 ft. long); beds ½ to 1 ft. thick; contains lenses of conglomerate at base; contains abundant mud pellets; contains plant stems and amphibian fauna (fauna O) in basal part; forms resistant ledge.. 2.0

6. Mudstone: pale reddish brown and yellowish gray, calcareous, crumbly, brittle; forms slope; largely concealed... 5.0

7. Limestone: yellowish gray, silty; similar to no. 5; contains intraformational conglomerate at base with ⅛ to ¼ in. rounded gravels; grades up into resistant, slightly calcareous, pale reddish-brown siltstone; contains medium-scale cross-laminae 4–10 ft. long; contains plant stems, reed impressions, *Chirotherium* tracks, swim marks, and amphibian remains (fauna P); forms prominent ledge (cap of escarpment).. 2.5

8. Siltstone: pale reddish brown, brittle, slightly calcareous, crumbly; contains 3 weak ledges (1–2 ft.) of:
Claystone: pale reddish brown to weak yellow, slightly calcareous, irregularly bedded;
Forms slope... 38.0

9. Claystone: pale reddish brown, calcareous, ripple-marked; forms ledge with bench above... 0.5

10. Mudstone: weak red and yellowish gray, brittle; like no. 6; forms slope......... 5.5

11. Claystone: very pale brown, slightly calcareous; like no. 9; beds ½–2 in.; contains abundant ripples; forms ledge.. 1.0

12. Claystone: weak reddish brown, locally yellowish gray, calcareous, brittle; contains lens of yellowish-gray, resistant siltstone up to 3 in. thick; forms slope.... 12.5

13. Siltstone: weak red, slightly calcareous, sandy; beds medium in thickness (½–1 ft.); contains ripple laminae; weathers weak reddish brown; forms resistant ledge with prominent bench above...................................... 2.0
                                          ————

    Total Holbrook member.. 98.5

Moqui member; units forming light olive-gray and very pale reddish-brown slopes:
14. Claystone: weak reddish brown and yellowish gray, calcareous, brittle, structureless (fissile and shaly in upper part); contains a few beds up to 1 in. thick; at 11 ft. contains 1-ft. ledge of:
Claystone: light brown to light olive gray, calcareous, ripple-laminated;
Forms slope... 26.5

15. Sandstone: pale brown, very fine-grained, slightly calcareous; beds medium in thickness (½–1 ft.); ripple-laminated throughout; forms resistant ledge........ 2.0

16. Siltstone: weak reddish brown and yellowish gray, calcareous, shaly, brittle; contains pockets of gypsum; forms top of "pink" series (middle member); forms slope; partly concealed... 16.5+
                                          ————

    Total Moqui member.. 45.0
    Total Moenkopi measured... 143.5

Concealed area developed in light olive-gray and very pale reddish-brown beds

Section 17.—*Cameron, Arizona*

Measured at Poverty Tank, 4 miles southwest of Cameron

Shinarump: massive conglomerate and cross-laminated sandstone.
Unconformity: irregular surface with relief up to 2 ft. in area examined.

Moenkopi formation:
  Holbrook member:

Feet

1. Siltstone: weak reddish brown, locally very light olive gray, thin-bedded (½–2 in.); uppermost 1 ft. structureless mudstone.................................... 3.0±

2. Mudstone: light brown, calcareous, sandy; beds irregular and moderately thick (½–2 ft.); weathers weak reddish brown; forms ledge....................... 3.0

3. Claystone: very light olive gray and weak reddish brown, calcareous, fissile; forms slope; contains a few thin ledges of more resistant light-brown mudstone like no. 2... 32.0

4. Siltstone: weak red, calcareous, cross-laminated; beds 3–8 ft. thick; contains mud-ball layer; contains plant impressions; weathers pale reddish brown or with weak brown varnish, massive; forms cliff (prominent marker bed)................... 14.0

5. Claystone: very light olive gray and weak reddish brown; and mudstone: light brown; like no. 3... 64.5

6. Siltstone: light brown, calcareous, weakly cross-laminated; weathers same color; forms prominent ledge... 5.5

Total Holbrook member.. 122.0

Moqui member:
7. Claystone: very light olive gray and weak reddish brown, fissile; like no. 1; no argillaceous odor noted; contains secondary gypsum in bedding planes and veins; contains more resistant beds 2–3 ft. thick of light-brown mudstone like no. 2.... 37.5

8. Siltstone: light brown, silty, calcareous; cross-laminated on small to medium scale; weathers pale brown to very pale reddish brown; forms ledge.............. 4.5

9. Siltstone: yellowish gray, calcareous, shaly, weak; weathers as very pale-brown layer conspicuous in section; forms slope.................................... 11.0

10. Siltstone: pale brown, cross-laminated, ledge forming; like no. 8................ 3.0

11. Siltstone: very light brown, calcareous, gypseous, thin-bedded, soft; contains a few more resistant beds; weathers same color; forms slope; largely concealed....... 6.0

12. Siltstone: light brownish gray, sandy, calcareous; beds thin and flat; shows ripple laminae; weathers very pale to pale brown; forms persistent ledge........... 4.5

13. Siltstone: very pale brown, shaly; like no. 9; gypseous in places; more resistant beds show ripple lamination; forms slope with several weak ledges............... 29.5

Total Moqui member.. 96.0

Wupatki member:
14. Siltstone: weak reddish brown, calcareous; cemented with iron oxide; beds thin and flat; weathers moderate to weak brown; forms slope....................... 7.5

15. Sandstone: pale red, very fine-grained, calcareous; large-scale cross-lamination weakly developed; weathers pale reddish brown, massive; forms prominent rounded cliff... 34.0+

16. Siltstone: weak reddish brown, calcareous, thin-bedded; forms slope............ 5.0

17. Mudstone: pale reddish brown, silty, calcareous, micaceous; beds thin (1–3 in.), gnarly, irregular; weathers same color; forms ledge....................... 3.5

18. Claystone: weak red with prominent bands of yellowish gray; structureless or with poorly developed flat beds; contains numerous thin siltstone beds like no. 14; largely concealed... 34.0

19. Siltstone: weak reddish brown, flat-bedded; like no. 14; forms persistent ledge..... 2.5

20. Claystone: weak red, flat-bedded; like no. 18; alternates with beds and lenses of: Claystone: weak red, calcareous; beds average 6–20 in.; contains moderate amounts of silt and, locally, mica flakes; shows shrinkage cracks and ripple marks; weathers weak reddish brown; becomes dominant sediment upward; Total forms slope... 32.0

Total Wupatki member..................................... 118.5
Total Moenkopi... 336.5

Unconformity: stripped surface along top of Kaibab limestone; relief of several feet shown locally by ledges above basal Moenkopi; no conglomerate observed.
Kaibab limestone: gray, crystalline, massive.

Section (Partial) 18.–*Tappan Wash, Arizona*

Measured 2.4 miles south of State Highway 64

Shinarump conglomerate
Unconformity: assumed

Moenkopi formation:
  Holbrook member:

	Feet
1. Mudstone (?): forms slope with ledges.	27.5
2. Sandstone: white*, structureless; forms ledge.	1.5
3. Mudstone (?): forms slope.	17.5
4. Siltstone: weak reddish brown; contains ripple marks; contains impression of plant stem; weathers to flat slabs.	11.0
5. Mudstone (?): contains numerous plant fragments; forms slope.	28.5
6. Siltstone: reddish gray, calcareous; alternates with: Sandstone: very pale orange, very fine-grained; contains plant fragments; contains ripple marks and shrinkage cracks; *Chirotherium barthi* horizon (fauna U); forms cliff.	6.5
7. Mudstone (?): forms slope.	13.0
8. Sandstone: white; forms ledge.	1.5
9. Mudstone (?): forms slope.	26.0
10. Sandstone: light brownish gray, fine-grained to silty, very calcareous, hard; weathers pale brown; forms ledge.	2.0±
Total Holbrook member.	135.0

Moqui member:
  11. Siltstone: very light yellowish brown, sandy, calcareous; weathers light yellowish brown to pale reddish brown; forms ledge. . . . . not measured.
* Except for beds 4, 6, 10, 11, color and texture not accurately determined.

Section (Partial) 19.—*Cameron, Arizona*

Measured near State Highway 64, 4.8 miles west of Cameron Jct.
Shinarump conglomerate:
  Conglomerate: moderate brown, cross-laminated to base; pebbles scattered sparingly throughout; weathers massive; forms cliff.
Unconformity: surface of small relief; channels 6–8 in. deep where exposed.

Moenkopi formation:
  Holbrook member:

	Feet
1. Siltstone: light brownish gray, calcareous, shaly; grades up into brittle, structureless siltstone; forms slope.	16.5
2. Siltstone: weak red, calcareous; beds flat to irregular; weathers moderately massive; forms ledge.	2.0
3. Mudstone: weak reddish brown, calcareous, shaly; contains a few thin beds of calcareous pale-brown siltstone; forms slope.	11.0
4. Sandstone: pale brown, very fine-grained, cross-laminated; weathers weak reddish brown; forms ledge.	4.5
5. Siltstone: weak reddish brown, micaceous, thin-bedded; forms slope.	12.0
6. Siltstone: weak reddish brown, micaceous; similar to no. 5 but not in thin beds; contains ripple marks throughout, mud pellet impressions near base, and fucoidal markings; contains bone fragments (fauna Q); forms prominent ledge.	7.0

7. Sandstone: weak red, very fine-grained; beds mostly very thin, flat; contains some

more massive cross-laminated beds; contains bone fragments (fauna R); locally
  contains:
Limestone: weak to dusky red, sandy; contains pelecypod shells (molds and calcite),
  amphibian bones, fish plates and spines (fauna S); 1½ ft.-bed at 3 ft. above base
  of unit;
Total.. 23.0

8. Sandstone: weak reddish brown, very fine-grained; similar to no. 7 but thicker-
   bedded; cross-laminated on large scale; weathers to thin flat slabs; contained two
   amphibian skulls (fauna T) near base; forms prominent ledge................. 9.5

9. Mudstone: very pale brown to light brown, shaly; contains a few thicker (½–1 in.),
   irregular beds; forms slope... 23.0

10. Siltstone: pale brown to weak red, micaceous, ripple-laminated; beds 1–3 in. thick;
    forms ledge.. 2.0

11. Mudstone: very light olive gray, crumbly, brittle; and
    Claystone: weak reddish brown
    Total forms much-concealed slope.. 7.0

12. Siltstone: very light yellowish brown, micaceous, resistant; cross-laminated on small
    scale; forms ledge... 2.0±

13. Slope: partly concealed; near top contains:
    Mudstone: weak reddish brown, crumbly
    Total.. 5.5

14. Siltstone: weak reddish brown, argillaceous, sandy, thin-bedded (½–2 in.), very
    hard; ripple-marked; weathers to large flagstone slabs; forms prominent ledge.... 2.5

15. Mudstone: weak reddish brown, shaly; forms slope......................... 4.0

16. Mudstone: weak reddish brown, structureless; weathers massive; forms rounded
    ledge... 1.5
                                                                         ─────
    Total Holbrook member... 133.0

Moqui member:
17. Mudstone: pale olive, shaly; alternates with:
    Claystone: light brown, shaly; and a few beds of:
    Mudstone: weak reddish brown, irregularly-bedded;
    Total forms slope.. 27.5
                                                                         ─────
    Total measured.. 160.5
Base concealed by alluvium in valley

SECTION 20.—*12 miles Northwest of Cameron, Arizona*
Measured 1 mile north of the Little Colorado

Shinarump formation:
  Conglomerate: coarse sandstone with many gravel lenses; poor sorting; cross-lamina-
    tion; fossils, petrified wood, and bone concentrations; weathers light brown;
    forms very resistant cliff
Unconformity: contact not exposed; basal Shinarump contains large (3–4 in.) fragments
  of Moenkopi

Moenkopi formation:
  Holbrook member:
                                                                          Feet
1. Mudstone: weak reddish brown, brittle; exposed at several horizons; forms slope;
   contains:
   Siltstone: weak red; ripple marks; forms 2-ft. ledge
   Total... 35.0

2. Mudstone: pale reddish brown; weak irregular beds; forms ledge............. 2.0

3. Mudstone: pale reddish brown, brittle; forms slope....................... 6.5

4. Siltstone: very pale orange to weak yellow, calcareous; flat-bedded (1–6 in.); locally
   ripple-marked; contains tracks; liesegang lines prominent; forms ledge........ 1.5

5. Mudstone: deep red, brittle, crumbly; forms slope........................ 3.0

Feet

6. Siltstone: pale reddish brown, calcareous; thick beds (2–4 ft.); contains rain pits, parallel ripple marks, shrinkage cracks; weathers to double cliff with a slope in the middle. 25.0

Total Holbrook member. 73.0

Moqui member:
7. Mudstone: weak reddish brown, structureless; forms slope; contains:
Siltstone: pale reddish brown, shaly; three 1-ft. beds; ripple marks
Total. 26.0

8. Limestone: light yellowish brown, silty; irregular bedding; like no. 12; weathers brown; contains salt molds; forms ledge. 1.5

9. Mudstone: weak reddish brown; slope alternating with thin (3–4 in.) limy siltstone like slope 11. . . . .   4.5

10. Siltstone: very pale brown, very calcareous; medium beds (1 ft.); weakly ripple-laminated, cusp ripple; weathers brown with flat surfaces. 1.0

11. Mudstone: weak reddish brown, brittle, crumbly; forms slope. 4.5

12. Limestone: light yellowish brown, silty, micaceous; irregular bedding; forms ledge. .   1.5

13. Mudstone: weak reddish brown, micaceous, brittle, crumbly; forms slope. 5.0

14. Siltstone: very pale orange, calcareous, very hard; thick-bedded (1–2 ft.); weakly laminated; cusp ripple marks; weathers brown; forms strong ledge. 3.5

15. Mudstone: weak reddish brown, brittle, crumbly; forms slope. 2.5

16. Siltstone: very pale brown to light yellowish brown, calcareous; medium beds (½–1 ft.); ripple marks (cusp and parallel); forms resistant ledges. 1.5

17. Claystone: weak reddish brown, micaceous, brittle, crumbly; forms slope. 4.5

18. Siltstone: very pale orange to very pale brown, calcareous, hard, shaly; weathers gray to purple; ripple-laminated throughout; forms steep slope. 10.0

Total Moqui member. 66.0

Wupatki member:
19. Sandstone: very pale orange, very fine-grained, slightly calcareous, massive; weathers to rounded "rock babies", honeycomb weathering; locally contains mud pellets up to 3 in. in diameter; forms rim of cliff. 5.5
Sandstone: very pale orange, very fine-grained; locally friable; weathers into thin flat beds with shaly appearance; forms cliff with units above and below locally; elsewhere forms bench. 19.5
Sandstone: very pale orange, mottled; massive; thick beds (2–10 ft.); flat and gnarly bedding in part, medium to large-scale cross-lamination in part; weathers to pale orange. 10.0
Siltstone: very pale orange, calcareous; thin (½–1 ft.) resistant beds; ripple-lamination; contains mud pellets and worm borings. 6.0
Total. 41.0

20. Siltstone: weak reddish brown, calcareous; slope of shaly siltstones and brittle mudstones like no. 22, but larger proportion of siltstone; parallel ripple marks and salt molds. 43.0

21. Siltstone: very pale orange, calcareous; thin-bedded, thicker-bedded at the top; upper 1½ ft. more massive; cross-lamination; abundant ripple marks, salt molds, mud pellets; forms moderately resistant ledge. 5.0

22. Mudstone: weak reddish brown, slightly calcareous, brittle, crumbly; thin beds and lenses of more resistant pale reddish-brown shaly siltstone alternating throughout; total forms slope. 19.0

23. Siltstone: pale reddish brown, shaly; wavy parallel ripple marks. 1.0

24. Concealed: slope; contains:
Claystone: very pale orange, calcareous, brittle, crumbly; 2 ft. thick; 4½ ft. from the base;
Mudstone: weak reddish brown, shaly, slightly calcareous; 35 ft. from the base;
Total. 40.5

Total Wupatki member. 190.5
Total Moenkopi. 329.5

Unconformity: even flat surface (for ¼ mile) where observed
Kaibab formation:
    Limestone: yellowish gray; medium-bedded (1–2 ft.); weathers very pale orange
    with a pitted surface

SECTION 21.—*20 miles West Shadow Mountain, Arizona*

Shinarump formation:
    Conglomerate: gray; coarse-grained sandstone matrix with scattered gravels up to
    3 in.; cross-lamination on large scale.
Unconformity: assumed

Moenkopi formation:
    Holbrook member:

	Feet
1. Mudstone: weak reddish brown, very thin and shaly; locally micaceous; forms slope	11.0
2. Siltstone: light brown, calcareous, micaceous; liesegang lines; cusp ripple marks; forms resistant ledge	1.0
3. Concealed: slope	13.0
4. Siltstone: pale brown, calcareous; locally micaceous; ripple cross-lamination throughout; massive resistant beds (½–2 ft.); cusp ripple marks; weathers weak reddish brown; forms prominent ledge	5.5
5. Partly concealed: slope; contains: Siltstone· pale reddish brown, slightly calcareous; thin irregular beds; forms a weak ledge; Mudstone: weak reddish brown, argillaceous Total	5.0
6. Siltstone: pale reddish brown, calcareous, hard; weathers weak reddish brown; forms resistant ledge	13.0
7. Siltstone: pale reddish brown, shaly; abundant ripple marks, mud cracks, worm trails; alternates with: Mudstone: weak reddish brown, crumbly, brittle; together with the above siltstone forms a recess	2.0
8. Siltstone: weak reddish brown, calcareous, micaceous; thick (2 ft.) beds; massive beds; forms resistant ledges	6.0
Total Holbrook member	56.5

    Moqui member:

	Feet
9. Mudstone: weak reddish brown, structureless; bed of cores-and-shells near the top; forms slope, largely concealed; contains: Siltstone: pale brown, shaly; ripple marks; forms a ledge half way up and another near the top Total	40.5
10. Siltstone: very pale brown, calcareous; like no. 12	1.0
11. Concealed: slope	7.0
12. Siltstone: very pale brown, calcareous; resistant beds (1–20 in.); cross-laminated locally; cusp ripple marks; forms ledge	3.5
13. Siltstone: very pale brown, calcareous; thin flat beds; locally cross-laminated; ripple marks; forms slope with weak ledges; partly concealed	12.0
14. Siltstone: very pale orange, shaly; thin flat beds; poorly exposed slope	2.0
Total Moqui member	66.0

Wupatki member:

	Feet
15. Sandstone: very pale orange, friable; cross-laminated on medium scale; much honeycomb weathering; thick rounded ledge at top receding from main cliff; forms sheer massive cliff	47.0
16. Mudstone: weak reddish brown, crumbly; with a few thin beds of siltstone; forms bench and recess	5.5

Feet

17. Siltstone: very pale orange to very pale brown, ripple laminated, thin-bedded (1/4–3 in.); weathers to very pale brown; forms slope..................... 4.0

18. Siltstone: very pale orange, micaceous, structureless; forms resistant rounded ledge... 2.0

19. Mudstone: weak reddish brown, crumbly; like no. 21........................ 1.0

20. Siltstone: very pale orange; ripple marks; forms weak ledges................. 1.5

21. Mudstone: weak reddish brown, crumbly; exfoliates into rounded masses; forms recess... 2.0

22. Mudstone: pale reddish brown, shaly; forms recess.......................... 2.5

23. Siltstone: light yellowish brown, hard, ripple-laminated; cusp ripple marks; forms resistant ledge... 2.0

24. Siltstone: pale reddish brown, calcareous; forms slope like no. 26............... 11.0

25. Siltstone: pale reddish brown, calcareous; salt molds; forms ledge like no. 27...... 4.5

26. Siltstone: pale reddish brown; like underlying but separated by a few thin units of: Mudstone: weak reddish brown, crumbly; Total forms slope with weak ledges..................................... 23.0

27. Siltstone: weak reddish brown; beds up to 2 in. thick; many parallel ripple marks; forms cliff... 5.0

28. Mudstone: weak reddish brown, crumbly, brittle; forms partly concealed slope; contains series of very weak ledges of: Siltstone: weak reddish brown, abundant parallel ripple marks, mud cracks, salt molds; proportion of siltstone increases upward Total... 55.0

29. Concealed: slope; contains a ledge of: Limestone: pale reddish mottled with white, argillaceous; 1 bed 2 in. thick; contains mud pellets and granules of chert; gradation into red-bed series.............. 2.0

Total Wupatki member.. 168.0

Limestone member:
30. Limestone: pale reddish brown; beds thin (1–3 in.) and flat; contains abundant scattered grains of quartz, jasper, and limestone up to granule size............ 3.0

31. Limestone: very pale orange to pale orange; beds 1–2 ft. thick; conglomeratic gravels (locally) up to 5 in. (at base), commonly 1/4–1/2 in., composed of angular chert, jasper, limestone pebbles, and coarse quartz grain concentrations........ 3.0

Total Limestone member... 6.0
Total Moenkopi measured.. 296.5

Unconformity: irregular surface relief of 1–2 ft. in lateral distance of 15 ft.
Kaibab formation:
  Limestone: very pale orange, crystalline, resistant; medium thickness (6–12 in.); weathers rough.

SECTION 22.—*The Gap, Arizona*
Measured 5.0 miles north of Gap, east of Highway 89
(Dip 5° northeast)

Shinarump conglomerate:
  Sandstone: light yellowish brown, medium- to coarse-grained, quartzitic, thick-bedded; contains layers of rounded pebbles; weathers yellowish brown to dark brown.
Unconformity: assumed

Moenkopi formation:
  Units forming upper series of cliffs and slopes:

Feet

1. Siltstone: pale reddish brown, very calcareous, shaly; forms slope.............. 11.0

2. Siltstone: very pale brown to light yellowish brown, very calcareous (especially at top), resistant; beds thin to irregular; weathers weak brown; forms ledge........ 12.0

Feet

3. Mudstone: weak to dusky red, crumbly, soft; forms slope.......................   10.0

4. Limestone: light brownish gray to light yellowish brown, silty, hard; beds thin
   (2–4 in.), flat; contains ripple marks on upper surface; weathers weak brown to
   black; forms ledge...   2.0

5. Claystone: weak reddish brown, very calcareous, brittle, crumbly; alternates with:
   Siltstone: light brown to light yellowish brown, very calcareous, resistant; beds
   ½–2 in. thick; contains ripple marks; weathers light brown; forms thin ledges
   Unit forms slope..   22.0

  Total upper series...   57.0

Massive cliff-forming unit:
6. Sandstone: light brownish gray to light yellowish brown, very fine-grained, argillaceous, calcareous, thick-bedded (2–4 ft.); cross-laminated on large scale; locally
   contains ripple marks; weathers dark brown, massive; forms resistant cliff......   30.5
Units forming lower series of slopes and ledges:

7. Claystone: light yellowish brown, very calcareous, shaly; contains ripple marks and
   mud pellets; forms resistant ledge..   8.5

8. Mudstone: weak red, calcareous, micaceous; alternates with:
   Mudstone: light brown (locally light yellowish brown in lower 10 ft.), calcareous,
   resistant, thin-bedded (1–3 in.);
   Unit contains ripple marks, molds of salt crystals, mud cracks; forms slopes (5–15 ft.)
   with series of ledges (1–3 ft.)...   89.0

9. Claystone: light olive gray, micaceous, fissile; alternates with:
   Mudstone: light yellowish brown, thin-bedded (¼–½ in.);
   Near center, unit contains:
   Limestone: dark gray, thin-bedded (1–4 in.); cross-laminated on small scale; con-
   tains silt curls
   Unit forms slope..   22.0

10. Claystone: dusky red, silty, calcareous, structureless, crumbly; locally weathers
    to rounded knobs; forms slope..   15.5

11. Mudstone: light olive gray, brittle, crumbly; contains a few beds of:
    Siltstone: light yellowish brown, very calcareous; beds up to ½ in. thick; resistant
    Unit forms slope...   9.5

12. Conglomerate..   0–2.5
    matrix: light brownish gray limestone;
    gravels: angular, up to 1 in. diameter, white to gray chert.

  Total lower series... 147.0
  Total Moenkopi.. 234.5

Unconformity: surface controlled by hard upper layer of Kaibab formation; fairly level
   where exposed
Kaibab formation:
   Siltstone: calcareous, massive; beds 6–10 in. thick; contains much chert

SECTION 23.—*Cedar Ridge, Arizona*

Measured 3.3 miles north of Cedar Ridge, .5 miles southwest of Highway 89

(Dip 12° north where measured. Beds 1–13 measured along strike)

Shinarump conglomerate:
   Sandstone: very pale brown, medium- to very coarse-grained, calcareous; cross-
      laminated on large scale; contains conglomerate layers throughout, and logs of
      petrified wood; weathers weak to moderate brown; forms cliff
Unconformity

Moenkopi formation:
   Units forming upper series of cliffs and slopes:

Feet

1. Mudstone to siltstone: weak reddish brown and very pale olive, shaly; alternates
   with:
   Siltstone: reddish gray, sandy, calcareous, thin-bedded;
   Forms slope, much concealed..   6.0

Feet

2. Siltstone: weak reddish brown, calcareous; cross-laminated on medium scale; weathers same color; forms weak ledge.................................... 6.0

3. Siltstone: pale to weak reddish brown; similar to no. 2 but shaly-bedded; forms slope... 5.5

4. Siltstone: weak reddish brown, very calcareous, structureless, thick-bedded; contains tracks of lacertoids, *Chirotherium* toe marks, and shrinkage cracks on under surface; weathers weak reddish brown, smooth; forms cliff with straight face.... 8.0

5. Claystone: dusky red, silty, crumbly, calcareous, soft near base, more resistant above; contains very pale-brown deoxidation blotches; contains very pale-brown, silty, micaceous limestone near top; forms slope; largely concealed............ 23.5

6. Siltstone: weak red, calcareous, structureless; weathers weak to dusky reddish brown, massive, rounded; forms ledge ("rock-baby" horizon?)................ 3.5

7. Mudstone: dusky red, calcareous, crumbly; alternates with:
Siltstone: light yellowish brown, calcareous, resistant; beds ¼–½ in. thick
Unit contains 1 thin (4 in.) bed of reddish-gray, very calcareous siltstone; forms slope, much concealed.................................... 14.5

        Total upper series.................................... 67.0

Massive cliff-forming unit:
8. Sandstone: very pale brown to light yellowish brown, medium-grained to silty (mostly fine-grained), very calcareous; cross-laminated on large scale; weathers moderate yellowish brown to weak reddish brown, massive; forms cliff........ 21.5

Units forming lower series of slopes and ledges:

9. Mudstone: brilliant reddish brown, micaceous, shaly, fissile; forms slope.......... 0.5

10. Siltstone: light yellowish brown, argillaceous, calcareous, shaly; contains molds of salt crystals; weathers same color; forms weak cliff......................... 5.5

11. Claystone: weak red, calcareous, crumbly; forms slope......................... 5.0

12. Mudstone: weak to pale reddish brown, calcareous, structureless; beds ½–2 ft. thick; weathers same color, massive; forms prominent ledge.................. 3.0

13. Claystone: weak red, crumbly; like no. 11; alternates with:
Mudstone: light brown, calcareous, shaly; contains casts of salt crystals (at about 55 ft.), abundant ripple marks, and mud cracks; forms ledges, thicker in upper part;
Unit forms slope with ledges.. 79.5

14. Limestone: very light to very pale brown, silty to sandy (locally grades to very fine-grained sandstone); beds irregular; contains abundant geodes; weathers light to pale brown; forms ledge.. 0.5

15. Mudstone: weak reddish brown, thin-bedded (1–3 in.); contains rain pits; alternates with:
Claystone: weak red, crumbly;
Like no. 13; forms series of ledges and slopes................................ 21.5

16. Claystone: weak red, crumbly; alternates with:
Siltstone: pale brown, locally sandy, calcareous (locally grades to limestone), ripple-marked; more abundant in center (55–66 ft.);
Unit similar to no. 13; forms slope, largely concealed near base................ 89.0

17. Limestone: weak red, coarsely crystalline, thin-bedded (1–2 in.); contains scattered quartz grains and clay pellets; weathers weak reddish brown; forms ledge...... 4.0

18. Mudstone: weak red, crumbly; and siltstone, very pale brown; like no. 16; forms slope... 21.5

19. Siltstone: very pale brown to light yellow, argillaceous, shaly; locally ripple-marked; forms slope; largely concealed..................................... 5.5

        Total lower units.................................... 235.5
        Total Moenkopi.................................... 324.0

Unconformity: contact not exposed

Kaibab formation:
Sandstone: very light yellowish brown, fine-grained, calcareous; contains geodes; weathers rough, massive

SECTION 24.—*Cedar Ridge, Arizona*

Measured 10 miles north of Cedar Ridge

(Dip 12° in beds 1–12 where measured, 6° in beds 13–18)

Shinarump conglomerate:
Sandstone: very pale brown, fine- to coarse-grained; locally contains pockets with gravels
Unconformity: thickness of uppermost Moenkopi bed decreases about 5 ft. in ¼ mi. westward along erosion surface

Moenkopi formation:
Units forming upper series of cliffs and slopes:

Feet

1. Largely concealed: slope; near center contains:
Siltstone: reddish gray, very calcareous, shaly
Total.. 17.5

2. Siltstone: weak reddish brown, calcareous, hard; beds 6–19 ft. thick; weathers same color, massive; forms cliff with straight face.............................. 19.5

3. Claystone: dusky red, calcareous, structureless, brittle, crumbly; weathers to rounded knobs; alternates with:
Mudstone: weak reddish brown; beds thin (1–2 in.), flat; contains ripple marks and shrinkage cracks
Total forms weak unit...................................... 16.5

4. Siltstone: weak reddish brown, calcareous, argillaceous, shaly; weathers weak reddish brown; forms slope; partly concealed................................. 16.5

5. Sandstone: pale red, very fine-grained, very calcareous, very hard, ripple-marked (cusp-type); beds 1–2 ft. thick; weathers weak reddish brown; forms resistant cliff with straight face (weathers to "rock babies")......................... 4.5

6. Sandstone: pale red, very fine-grained, silty, like no. 4; forms slope, largely concealed.. 19.5

7. Sandstone: pale red, very fine-grained, calcareous, flat-bedded, resistant; weathers weak brown to dusky red; forms cliff.................................... 4.0

8. Sandstone: pale red, very fine-grained, silty, calcareous, shaly, forms slope........ 6.5

Total upper series.. 104.5

Massive cliff-forming unit:
9. Sandstone: very light yellowish brown, very fine-grained, calcareous, ripple-marked; cross-laminated on large scale; weathers weak brown to light yellowish brown, massive, honeycombed; forms rounded cliff.............................. 16.5

10. Sandstone: very light yellowish brown; like no. 9 but beds thin (2–6 in.) and flat; forms ledge.. 4.5

Total massive cliff unit.. 21.0

Units forming lower series of slopes and ledges:
11. Siltstone: very light yellowish brown, shaly, very calcareous; contains a few more resistant beds ¼–1 in. thick; forms slope.................................... 11.0

12. Mudstone: weak reddish brown, calcareous (locally grades to limestone); ripple-marked, beds thin (¼–2 in.) and flat; weathers pale reddish brown; forms weak cliffs (1–4 ft.); alternates with:
Mudstone: weak reddish brown, brittle, crumbly; forms slopes (3–10 ft.)
Total contains selenite veins cutting beds and following bedding planes; some beds very gypseous.. 83.5

13. Claystone: weak reddish brown, silty, calcareous, crumbly, brittle; contains a few ledges of:
Mudstone: weak red, calcareous, thin-bedded (⅛–¼ in.), resistant,
Total forms slope... 42.0

14. Limestone: pale brown, silty, micaceous, resistant; ripple-marked (cusp type, locally cut subsequently by shrinkage cracks); forms ledge.................... 0.5

15. Claystone and mudstone: like no. 13; contains pale-brown to dusky red impure limestone concretions; forms slope.. 5.0

Feet

16. Limestone: pale brown, silty, like no. 14; ripple-marked throughout (cusp type); contains silty limestone cores-and-shells; forms ledge........................ 1.0

17. Claystone and mudstone: like no. 13; forms slope............................ 77.5

18. Mudstone: light yellowish brown (locally weak red), calcareous, shaly; forms slope... 5.5–10.5

       Total lower series.. 231.0
       Total Moenkopi.. 356.5

Unconformity: surface controlled by resistant Kaibab surface, giving steplike development with Moenkopi shales filling depression; relief of at least 5 ft. observed.
Kaibab formation:
     Sandstone: brilliant yellowish brown, very fine-grained, calcareous; beds thick (4–6 ft.), massive; contains chert beds; weathers strong yellowish brown.

Section 25.—*Shinumo Altar, Arizona*
Measured on south side of Shinumo Altar

Shinarump conglomerate:
     Conglomerate: pebbles up to ½ in.; very abundant; cross-lamination prominent; forms high massive cliff.
Unconformity: assumed

Moenkopi formation:
     Units forming upper series of cliffs and slopes:

Feet

1. Mudstone: weak reddish brown with streaks of pale olive; forms slope, largely concealed
At 44 ft., locally contains:
Siltstone: weak reddish brown; thin irregular bed; forms weak ledges
Total...................... 53.0

2. Siltstone: weak reddish brown, micaceous; prominent cliff formed of two thick beds (2–3 ft.) overlain by one very massive bed; forms "rock babies"; weathers dusky reddish-brown to black varnish.................................... 13.5

3. Claystone: weak reddish brown, calcareous; forms slope; contains:
Siltstone: pale reddish brown, calcareous; one thin ledge
Total....................... 35.0

4. Siltstone: weak reddish brown, calcareous; like no. 6 but flat-bedded; contains ripple laminae; parallel ripple marks; forms ledge......................... 2.5

5. Concealed: slope... 13.5

6. Siltstone: very pale brown to pale brown, calcareous, massive; cross-lamination medium scale, scour-and-fill type; weathers to weak reddish brown; forms prominent cliff.. 11.0

7. Mudstone: weak reddish brown, crumbly; forms slope with a ledge in the middle of:
Siltstone: very pale brown to pale brown, calcareous
Total....................... 18.5

       Total upper series.. 147.0

Massive cliff-forming unit:
8. Sandstone: very pale orange, very fine-grained; massive; 1 bed 3 ft. thick; laminae horizontal; long parallel ripple marks; weathers with a black varnish or a yellow surface
Sandstone: very pale orange, very fine-grained; weakly cross-laminated on large scale; weathers brown to yellow; forms massive cliff
Total....................... 25.0
Units forming lower series of slopes with ledges:

9. Siltstone: very pale orange; similar to underlying except for color.............. 7.0

10. Claystone and siltstone: steep slope similar to underlying except proportion of claystone to siltstone about equal; gypsum veins more common................. 28.5

11. Siltstone: pale reddish brown, shaly; ripple marks; forms ledges separated by:

Feet

Mudstone: pale reddish brown; thin beds; contains a few gypsum veins
Total forms steep slope. 66.0

12. Mudstone: weak reddish brown, crumbly, brittle; forms slope, partly concealed; at 33 ft. contains a 2½-ft. ledge of:
Siltstone: pale reddish brown; parallel ripple marks and mud cracks; at 52.5 ft. contains a ledge of:
Siltstone: pale reddish brown; same as previous ledge; at 56.5 ft. contains a ledge of:
Siltstone: pale reddish brown; same as previous 2 ledges
Total. 65.5

13. Siltstone: weak reddish brown, calcareous; thin-to medium-bedded (1–12 in.); ripple-laminated; cusp ripple marks prominent; contains casts of reptile tracks. . 2.5

14. Mudstone: weak reddish brown; with a few thin ledges of siltstone; forms slope like no. 16. . . . . 22.0

15. Siltstone: weak reddish brown, calcareous; contains mud cracks; forms thin ledge. . . 0.5

16. Mudstone: pale reddish brown to weak reddish brown, weak, crumbly, brittle; forms slope. 22.0

17. Concealed: slope. 38.5

18. Siltstone: pale reddish brown, calcareous, flat-bedded; contains a few very small chert fragments; forms resistant ledge. 1.5

19. Siltstone: weak orange, shaly; contains small scattered white chert fragments in lower part; forms slope. 3.5
Note: Above two beds are replaced along strike by thick resistant beds of cherty conglomerate.

Total lower series. 257.5

Basal conglomerate:
20. Conglomerate: mottled light orange, thin-bedded (2–6 in.), irregularly bedded; contains angular fragments of white chert and blue quartz up to 2 in. in diameter; matrix is a limy siltstone. 11.5
Total Moenkopi measured. 441.0
Unconformity: assumed
Kaibab formation:
Limestone: very pale orange to pale reddish brown, silty; beds (6 in.–1 ft.) thick; contains concretions and geodes; weathers rough and pitted. 4.0
Limestone: very pale orange, massive, silty; irregular surface; contains geodes and concretions; weathers weak orange to pale reddish brown.

SECTION 26.—*Navajo Bridge, Arizona*

Measured 9 miles southwest of Navajo Bridge, promontory east of road.

(Dip 2° east where measured)

Shinarump conglomerate:
Sandstone: white to yellowish brown, coarse-grained, quartzitic, cross-laminated; contains lenses of gravel near base; weathers brown; forms massive cliff.
Unconformity: in ¼ mi. ne., pre-Shinarump erosion has removed uppermost five beds of Moenkopi, and Shinarump there rests on bed 6; 1-ft. deoxidation zone of green shale at contact.

Moenkopi formation:
Units forming upper series of cliffs and slopes:

Feet

1. Mudstone: weak reddish brown, shaly, ripple-marked; alternates with:
Claystone: dusky red, structureless, crumbly
Total forms slope. 26.0

2. Siltstone: weak red, calcareous, shaly, resistant; forms cliff. 8.5

3. Claystone: weak reddish brown, structureless, and:
Mudstone: weak reddish brown, shaly; like no. 1; forms slope. 11.0

Total upper series. 45.5

Feet

Massive cliff-forming unit:
 4. Siltstone: light gray, coarse-grained; thick-bedded (2 beds 6–8 ft. thick), cross-laminated; weathers pale reddish brown; forms cliff...... 21.0
 5. Limestone: very light yellowish brown, aphanitic, silty, flat-bedded, weathers yellowish brown to brownish gray; two beds 2–3 ft. thick separated by:
  Mudstone: light olive gray, crumbly, structureless
  Total...... 9.5

   Total massive cliff unit...... 30.5

Units forming lower series of slopes with ledges:
 6. Mudstone: weak red to very pale brown, shaly; and:
  Claystone: dusky red, crumbly; like no. 1; total contains pink gypsum nodules and selenite veins throughout; forms slope or weak cliff...... 19.5

 7. Siltstone: weak reddish brown, shaly, locally ripple-marked; near base contains numerous thin (½–1 ft.) beds of:
  Limestone: light brown, aphanitic, silty and very argillaceous, resistant; weathers yellow with thin wavy laminae etched out
  Total contains:
  Mudstone: light brown; contains claystone and limestone pellets;
  Total forms slope...... 58.0

 8. Mudstone: weak reddish brown, shaly to structureless; and
  Claystone: dusky red, shaly to structureless; like no. 1; alternates with:
  Siltstone: weak to pale brown, very calcareous (grades into silty limestone), shaly, ripple-marked; forms ledges in lower 45 ft.
  Total contains argillaceous pale-brown limestone bed at 115 ft. above base, silt curls at 187 ft., gypsum nodules and veins of selenite; lower part of unit forms slope with thin ledges, grading up (above 247 ft.) to weak cliff as structureless units become more abundant...... 402.5

 9. Siltstone: yellowish gray, shaly; contains some thin-bedded (¼–½ in.) resistant siltstone; forms slope...... 6.5
Basal conglomerate:

 10. Conglomerate: beds ½–1 ft. thick; forms ledge...... 9.0
  matrix: very light yellowish brown, very calcareous, sandy siltstone;
  gravels: angular, up to 1 in. diameter but mostly ¼ in., mostly white chert.

  Total lower series...... 495.5
  Total Moenkopi...... 571.5
Unconformity: assumed
Kaibab limestone:
 Limestone: weak yellow, aphanitic, silty and very argillaceous, thin-bedded; contains irregularly shaped chert concretions resting on massive Kaibab beds

SECTION 27.—*Navajo Bridge, Arizona*

Measured 1.8 miles south of Navajo Bridge

(Dip 3° where measured)

Shinarump conglomerate:
 Conglomerate:
  matrix: white to yellowish brown, medium- to coarse-grained, calcareous sandstone;
  gravels: coarse, well rounded;
  cross-laminated on large scale; weathers weak reddish brown to very pale brown; forms massive cliff.
Unconformity: Moenkopi thickens approximately 50 ft. in ½ mi. s., as shown by addition of new units beneath Shinarump, seen where section is continuously exposed

Moenkopi formation:
 Massive cliff-forming unit:

Feet

 1. Mudstone: dusky red to very pale olive, calcareous, micaceous, shaly to weakly bedded; locally removed by erosion...... 0–2.0

 2. Sandstone: weak red, very fine-grained, thick-bedded; lower ⅔ cross-laminated,

Feet

massive; upper ⅓ thick, flat-bedded; weathers with weak reddish-brown varnish; forms massive cliff with straight faces and angular corners............. 38.0

3. Siltstone: very pale brown to very pale red; calcareous; beds 2–4 ft. thick; alternates with:
Mudstone: dusky red, structureless, weak; beds ½–1 ft.; weathers knobby
Total forms cliff.. 13.0

Total massive cliff unit... 53.0

Units forming lower series of slopes with ledges:
4. Claystone: dusky red, crumbly, brittle, fissile to structureless and knobby; contains much gypsum throughout (makes unit resistant); contains a few thin resistant beds of pale-brown calcareous mudstone 122 ft. above base; weathers to light and dark bands depending on surface staining; locally forms weak cliff........ 164.0

5. Claystone: dusky red, fissile, and mudstone: pale reddish brown; like no. 4 but with mudstone forming a series of weak ledges with thin beds of claystone forming slopes between... 27.5

6. Claystone: dusky red, calcareous, fissile; beds 2–8 ft. thick; alternates with:
Claystone: weak to pale reddish brown, crumbly, structureless; weathers pale reddish brown; forms weak ledges; also occurs as thin beds and lenses in dusky red claystone
Total contains layers of gypsum nodules and selenite veins increasing in abundance upward; forms slope.. 110.0

7. Limestone: weak reddish brown, finely crystalline, impure, silty, thin-bedded (½–2 in.); contains ripple marks; weathers same color; forms ledge........... 1.0

8. Claystone: dusky red, brittle, slope-forming; like no. 4......................... 24.0
9. Sandstone: brownish gray, very calcareous, argillaceous; beds thin (¼–½ in.), flat; weathers moderate brown, forms ledge........................... 0.2

10. Claystone: weak reddish brown, calcareous, crumbly, brittle; like no. 4; forms slope; alternates with:
Siltstone: pale reddish brown, calcareous; beds thin and flat; forms a few ledges 1–6 inches thick
Total... 46.5

11. Siltstone: pale reddish brown, argillaceous, calcareous; beds thin (¼–1 in.) and flat; forms ledge... 1.0

12. Mudstone: yellowish gray (locally pale reddish brown in upper part), sandy, crumbly, shaly; contains thin (1–2 in.) beds of:
Siltstone: very light yellowish brown, argillaceous, calcareous
Total forms slope... 5.5

13. Sandstone: weak yellow, very fine-grained, silty to argillaceous, very calcareous; contains scattered patches of angular conglomerate with fragments of white and light yellowish-brown chert up to ½ in. in diameter.

Total lower series... 379.7
Total Moenkopi.. 432.7+
Unconformity: general flat surface controlled by massive beds below
Kaibab limestone

SECTION 28.—*Lees Ferry, Arizona*

Measured 1 mile southwest of Lees Ferry, west of Colorado River

Shinarump conglomerate:
Sandstone: very pale brown, medium- to coarse-grained, structureless, resistant; contains lenses and pellets of green shale near base; contains coarse gravels scattered throughout; weathers pale brown; forms massive cliff.
Unconformity: erosion surface with considerable local relief (small hills up to 5 ft. high at contact where examined) and much greater relief seen in distance.
Moenkopi formation:
Units forming upper cliffs:

Feet

1. Mudstone: light brown, shaly; beds 1–3 ft. thick; alternates with:
Claystone: weak reddish brown, structureless of weakly bedded; beds 2–24 inches thick
Total forms weak cliff.. 44.0

Feet

2. Claystone: weak reddish brown, silty, crumbly, calcareous, structureless; alternates with:
Mudstone: light brown, calcareous, hard; beds thin (⅛–¼ in.)
Total similar to no. 1 but with less mudstone; forms slope.................... 55.5

3. Claystone and mudstone: like nos. 1 and 2 but with more claystone: locally deoxidized to light olive gray; contains beds of gypsum, impure limestone, concretions of gypsum, and selenite veins; locally contains ripple marks; shows increase in mudstone beds upward; forms weak cliff................................... 143.0

Units forming center slope:

4. Claystone and mudstone: like no. 1 but almost entirely claystone; contains light-brown or light yellowish-brown mudstone beds 1–2 in. thick at intervals of 30–40 ft.; total forms gentle slope..................... 93.5

5. Claystone and mudstone: like no. 1; contains more mudstone than no. 4; forms steep slope.................................. 93.5

Units forming lower cliff or steep slope:

6. Siltstone: pale reddish brown, calcareous; beds thin (4–8 in.) and flat; beds separated by thin zones (2–12 in.) of:
Claystone: weak reddish brown, crumbly;
total contains 4 thin beds of:
Conglomerate: locally ripple-marked
matrix: weak red calcareous siltstone;
gravels: up to 2 inches, angular, largely white chert, with rare light yellowish brown limestone
Total forms weak cliff...................................... 22.0

7. Mudstone: weak yellow, calcareous, fissile; forms slight recess; contains a few beds of:
Siltstone: very pale brown, calcareous, resistant; beds 1–2 in. thick; cross-laminated on small scale
Total.. 6.5

8. Conglomerate: fills erosion channels.................................. 5.5–22.0
matrix: light yellowish-brown calcareous siltstone;
gravels: up to 10 in. diameter, angular to subangular, poorly sorted, largely white chert with some light yellowish brown dolomite.

Total Moenkopi.. 480.0

Unconformity: surface eroded in channels with relief up to 30 ft., filled with conglomerate
Kaibab limestone:
Claystone: yellowish white, calcareous, hard, massive

Section 29.—*Vermilion Cliffs, Arizona*

Measured 2½ miles west of Navajo Bridge

(Dip 2° north)

Shinarump conglomerate:
Conglomerate: grayish brown, massive
Unconformity: surface very irregular with channels 10 ft. deep in siltstone
Moenkopi formation:
Units forming upper series of cliffs and slopes:

Feet

1. Limestone: light brownish gray, silty, hard; beds 2–5 ft. thick; contains casts of mud balls, tracks (?); weathers with desert varnish; forms resistant cliff with straight face...est. 30.0

2. Siltstone: weak reddish brown, calcareous; beds moderately thick (1–3 ft.); contains large ripple marks and reptile tracks; forms slope with weak cliff at center...est. 50.0

Total upper series... 80.0

Massive cliff-forming unit:

3. Sandstone: very pale orange, very fine-grained; cross-laminated on large scale; weathers with light-brown stain; forms massive cliff with straight face......est. 20.0

Units forming lower series of slopes with ledges:

Feet

4. Mudstone: yellowish gray, shaly; beds 1–2 ft. thick; contains shrinkage cracks;
   alternates with:
   Claystone: weak reddish brown, structureless, hard; beds ½–2 ft. thick; weathers to
   rounded knobs
   Total.. 29.5

5. Claystone: weak reddish brown; contains gypsum veins and seams throughout;
   forms cliff.. 66.0

6. Mudstone: light yellowish brown, gypsiferous; forms slope...................... 120.0

7. Mudstone: light brown; similar to no. 5 but contains more gypsum; contains beds
   of yellow siltstone; forms cliff more prominent than that of no. 5.............. 26.5

8. Mudstone: light yellowish brown; contains veins and seams of gypsum; like no. 6;
   forms steep slope and weak cliffs... 77.0

9. Claystone: weak reddish brown, calcareous; forms long slopes; alternates with:
   Mudstone: pale brown, very calcareous; like no. 8; contains ripple marks; forms thin
   ledges, widely separated;
   At top contains:
   Siltstone: light yellowish brown; forms 2-in. bed (marker bed)
   Total.. 66.0

10. Mudstone: weak reddish brown, calcareous, fissile; forms long slope; alternates
    with:
    Mudstone: light brown, calcareous, resistant; forms ledges 1–6 in. thick at intervals
    of 3–8 ft.;
    At 23.5 ft. contains 6-in. ledge of:
    Siltstone: light yellowish brown; contains ripple marks and mud pellets
    Total forms slope.. 41.5

11. Siltstone: light yellowish brown, sandy, calcareous, thin-bedded (1–3 in.) and lo-
    cally fissile; contains large and small current-type ripple marks; weathers light
    brown; forms weak cliff.. 32.0

12. Conglomerate:
    matrix: weak yellow siltstone;
    gravels: angular fragments, mostly ¼–½ in., white and light-gray chert;
    2–3 inch beds alternate with:
    Siltstone: weak yellow, shaly; beds 6–12 in.
    Total.. 2.5

    Total lower series... 461.0
    Total Moenkopi.. 561.0
Unconformity: small depressions in Kaibab filled with conglomerate
Kaibab formation:
    Chert: white; forms massive ledge; interbedded with small amount of:
    Limestone: weak yellow

Section 30.—*Vermilion Cliffs, Arizona*

Measured at Soap Creek, 8.8 miles west of Navajo Bridge

Shinarump conglomerate:
    Conglomerate: forms massive cliff;
        matrix: light brown, very coarse sand;
        gravels: mostly ¼–½ in., rounded gravels of durable material; scattered through-
        out basal part
Unconformity: 100 yards to north, base of Shinarump rises approximately 100 ft. reveal-
    ing addition of weak reddish-brown shaly siltstones; 50 yards to south Shinarump
    cuts out all Moenkopi deposits to base of light yellowish-brown mudstones (bed 6)
Moenkopi formation:
    Units forming upper slope:

Feet

1. Siltstone: weak reddish brown, shaly; beds thin (¼–½ in.) and flat; forms slope.... 16.5
Massive cliff-forming unit:

2. Sandstone: very pale orange, very fine-grained, calcareous, friable; cross-laminated
   on large scale; weathers light brown; forms massive cliff with sheer face........ 16.0

Feet

3. Limestone: very pale orange, finely crystalline, silty; beds ½–1 ft. thick; weathers with light-brown stain and with wavy laminations etched out.................. 5.5

Total massive cliff unit... 21.5

Units forming lower series of slopes with ledges:

4. Mudstone: light yellowish brown, structureless; weathers to rounded blocks; forms recess... 2.0

5. Mudstone: light yellowish brown, shaly (beds ¼–¾ in. thick); forms steep slope.. 24.0

6. Mudstone: light brown and light yellowish brown, shaly to fissile; forms weak ledges.. 5.5

7. Mudstone: pale reddish brown, calcareous, shaly; forms slope with ledge near center... 27.5

8. Mudstone: light brown, structureless to thin-bedded; contains prominent gypsum veins; forms series of cliff and slopes.................................. 176.0

9. Claystone: weak reddish brown, brittle; forms slope; alternates with:
   Siltstone: light yellowish brown and pale reddish brown, very calcareous (locally grades to limestone), hard; thin-bedded; forms thin ledges (2–3 in.) scattered at 2–4 ft. intervals
   Total... 27.5

10. Claystone: weak reddish brown, structureless; contains veins and seams of gypsum; alternates with:
    Siltstone: pale reddish brown, very calcareous, thin-bedded (½–1 in.); forms cliffs 5–15 ft. thick
    Forms series of cliffs and slopes similar to no. 8 but with smaller cliffs........... 44.0

11. Mudstone: light brown, fissile, shaly; alternates with:
    Siltstone: reddish gray, very calcareous (locally a silty limestone), thin-bedded (¼–½ in.); contains ripple marks; occurs at intervals of 3–9 ft.
    Forms steep slope with ledges.................................. 51.5

12. Claystone: weak reddish brown, structureless, brittle; forms slope; alternates with:
    Mudstone: light brown, very calcareous; contains ripple marks; forms ledges (2–5 in.) at intervals of 3–15 ft.
    Center part of unit much concealed.............................. 55.0

13. Limestone: light yellowish brown, silty, thin-bedded (½–2 in.); forms resistant ledge (marker bed)... 0.5

14. Mudstone: weak reddish brown, calcareous, friable, shaly; alternates with:
    Mudstone: weak reddish brown, resistant; forms ledges
    Total... 13.0

15. Siltstone: pale reddish brown, shaly, ripple-marked; forms weak ledges or slope... 5.0

16. Siltstone: very pale brown, shaly; weathers light brown..................... 3.0

17. Conglomerate.. 9.0
    matrix: light yellow, very fine-grained sandstone;
    gravels: angular pebbles of quartz, flint, chert, and other durable rocks averaging ½ in. diameter

Total lower series.. 460.0
Total Moenkopi... 498.0

Unconformity: assumed
Kaibab formation:
   Limestone: very pale orange, finely crystalline; beds thin and irregular; weathers rough; forms cliff

SECTION (Partial) 31.—*Vermilion Cliffs, Arizona*

Measured 13 miles west of Navajo Bridge, north of Highway 89

Shinarump conglomerate:
   Conglomerate:
      matrix: medium-grained but poorly sorted, very pale-brown sandstone; contains lenses of gravels as well as scattered gravels;
      gravels: pebbles up to ½ in. in diameter, of quartz and other durable materials

Feet

Unconformity:
 Beveled surface along tilted beds of Moenkopi in half mile horizontal distance
Moenkopi formation:
Upper red member:
1. Siltstone: reddish gray, calcareous (locally grades to light olive-gray limestone), resistant; beds 6–24 in. thick; weathers with desert varnish; forms cliff with straight face; alternates with:
Claystone: very pale brown, crumbly, ripple-marked; forms slopes 5–15 ft. thick
Total... 79.0

2. Siltstone: light brown, very calcareous; contains selenite veins; occurs as 2 massive beds; forms cliff with straight face but rounded at top...................... 23.0

3. Mudstone: pale brown, calcareous, brittle; forms slope; alternates with:
Siltstone: light brown to very light olive gray, very calcareous; forms thin (2–8 in.) ledges
Contains gypsum concretions and vein....................................... 51.0

4. Sandstone: pale brown, very fine-grained, slightly calcareous, hard; beds 3–5 ft. thick; contains ripple marks on upper surface; forms resistant ledge............ 12.0

 Total upper red member.. 165.0
Shnabkaib member:

5. Siltstone: yellowish gray, structureless, friable; forms weak ledge................ 6.5

6. Sandstone: very pale orange, very fine-grained, calcareous, quartzitic; beds thin (½–2 in.); alternates with:
Siltstone: very pale brown, slightly calcareous, shaly, hard; forms slope
Total.. 4.5

7. Gypsum: very pale orange; cross-laminated on large scale throughout (probably dune type); occurs as thick massive bed; forms cap of mesa................... 13.0

8. Claystone: light yellowish brown, silty, shaly; contains ripple marks and shrinkage cracks; forms steep slope or, locally, cliff of thick rounded beds beneath caprock.. 45.0

9. Mudstone: light brown, shaly; forms 3 ledges separated by:
Siltstone: light brown, gypseous; forms slopes
Total.. 44.0

 Total Shnabkaib member.. 113.0
Middle red member:

10. Mudstone: pale to light brown, shaly; impregnated with gypsum................ 19.5

11. Claystone: light brown, shaly; forms slope; alternates with:
Claystone: weak reddish brown; forms ledges (1–3 ft.) containing shaly siltstone and made resistant by gypsum
Total.. 55.0

12. Claystone: light brown; forms ledges; alternates with:
Claystone: light brown, weak, shaly, gypseous; forms slopes
Total.. 22.0

13. Claystone: weak reddish brown, poorly bedded (shaly toward top); locally very hard and concretionary, elsewhere crumbly; contains gypsum veins; weathers to knobby surface; forms major cliff...................................... 33.0

14. Claystone: weak reddish brown, brittle; forms slope; alternates with:
Mudstone: light brown, resistant, shaly; forms thin ledges at 3–8 ft. intervals..... 21.0

15. Limestone: very pale brown, silty; forms persistent ledge...................... 0.5

16. Siltstone: light brown; contains gypsum; forms slope......................... 10.0

17. Mudstone: weak reddish brown, poorly bedded to structureless; impregnated with gypsum and cut by gypsum veins; forms weak ledge...................... 4.5

18. Claystone: weak reddish brown; forms slope; alternates with:
Siltstone: weak orange, shaly; like no. 16; beds thin (⅛–¼ in.); forms numerous ledges distributed throughout unit.. 16.0

19. Mudstone: very pale brown, shaly, ripple-marked; forms ledge (marker bed) persistent for at least 1 mile... 0.1

Feet

20. Claystone: weak reddish brown, crumbly; contains selenite veins and seams throughout; forms slope..exposed   5.0

Total middle red member... 186.6
Total Moenkopi measured... 464.6
Base concealed

SECTION (Partial) 32.—*Vermilion Cliffs, Arizona*

Measured 18 miles west of Navajo Bridge, south of Highway 89

(Dip 10° northwest)

Chinle formation:
    Marl: light yellowish brown; contains petrified wood and lenses of gravel
Unconformity: entire upper red member removed by erosion 1 mi. to n., so that Chinle rests on Shnabkaib member
Moenkopi formation:
    Upper red member:

Feet

1. Siltstone: pale reddish brown, argillaceous, calcareous, thin-bedded; forms ledge....   18.0

2. Siltstone: pale reddish brown, argillaceous; like no. 1; forms ledge..............   2.0

3. Mudstone: weak reddish brown, calcareous, crumbly, brittle; forms slope......... 10.0

4. Siltstone: pale reddish brown, calcareous; weathers to thin (1/16–1/4 in.) flat beds; forms slope (locally structureless, resistant, forming cliff)..................... 17.0

5. Claystone: weak reddish brown, silty, calcareous, brittle, crumbly; forms slope; near center contains:
   Siltstone: light brown, argillaceous, calcareous, shaly; forms slope
   Total... 15.0

6. Mudstone: light brown, calcareous; forms massive cliff........................ 13.0

7. Siltstone: pale reddish brown, argillaceous, calcareous, crumbly, thin-bedded; contains more clay than underlying; forms slope...............................   5.0

8. Siltstone: light brown, calcareous; like no. 6; weathers weak reddish brown; forms resistant, massive cliff with straight face and angular corners................   6.5

Total upper red member.. 86.5
Shnabkaib member:

9. Claystone: weak reddish brown, calcareous, brittle, structureless; forms slope; alternates with:
   Claystone: light olive gray, silty, calcareous, shaly; forms thin (1–4 in.) resistant ledges at intervals of 3–15 ft.
   Contains numerous gypsum concretions and lenses............................ 49.5

10. Claystone: light olive gray, gypseous, shaly; weathers to white mounds; forms slope.. 11.0

11. Siltstone: very light olive gray, sandy, slightly calcareous, gypseous, shaly; weathers to very pale brown soil; forms slope; largely concealed......................   5.5

12. Sandstone: weak yellow, very fine-grained, calcareous, friable; cross-laminated on large scale; contains selenite veins; forms cliff............................ 17.5

13. Sandstone: weak yellow, very fine-grained, silty, gypseous, friable; alternates with: Siltstone: very pale olive gray, shaly; contains sand concretions 1/2 in. in diameter. 11.0

14. Mudstone: very light olive gray, shaly; forms ledge.........................   1.0

15. Siltstone: very light olive gray, friable; beds thin (1/8–1/2 in.) and flat; cut by veins and seams of selenite; forms slope....................................... 11.0

16. Mudstone: very light olive gray, shaly; like no. 14.........................   4.5

Total Shnabkaib member... 111.0
Total Moenkopi measured.. 197.5
Base concealed

SECTION (Partial) 33.— *Fredonia, Arizona*

Measured 3 miles east of Fredonia, 1 mile north of Highway 89

(Dip 5° where measured)

Shinarump conglomerate:
  Conglomerate:
    matrix: coarse sandstone, cross-laminated on large scale;
      gravel: scattered layers almost to base
Unconformity: evidence of local channelling
Moenkopi formation:
  Upper red member; units forming upper series of weak reddish-brown cliffs and slopes:

		Feet
1.	Siltstone: yellowish white, shaly; probable surface of deoxidation; forms slope	1.0
2.	Siltstone: light yellowish brown, calcareous, shaly, ripple-marked; alternates with: Mudstone: weak reddish brown, shaly, calcareous; forms slope	33.0
3.	Siltstone: weak reddish brown, calcareous, structureless to weakly bedded; weathers weak red, massive; forms ledge	6.5
4.	Siltstone: weak reddish brown, shaly; contains 3-in. bed of resistant, very light yellowish-brown, very fine-grained sandstone at center; like no. 2; forms slope, much concealed	15.5
5.	Siltstone: light brown, structureless, calcareous; like no. 3; two thick beds (6 and 15 ft. thick) separated by thinner ripple-marked beds of similar type; forms cliff	29.0
6.	Claystone: weak reddish brown, silty, calcareous, resistant, ripple-marked; beds 2–18 in. thick; alternates with: Claystone: dusky red, silty, crumbly; total forms weak cliff	8.0
7.	Siltstone: weak reddish brown to light brown, resistant; dominant type in lower part; alternates with: Claystone: dusky red and light olive gray, silty, crumbly; and Siltstone: very light olive gray, very friable Forms slope	80.0
8.	Sandstone: very pale brown, very fine-grained, resistant; beds thin (1–3 in.); weathers pale brown to weak reddish brown; forms ledge	0.5

Total upper red member 173.5

Shnabkaib member; units forming light olive-gray cliffs and slopes:

		Feet
9.	Mostly concealed: weak slope; contains a few ledges of: Siltstone: very pale olive, coarse-grained, ripple-marked Total	33.0
10.	Sandstone: very light olive gray, very fine-grained, calcareous, gypsiferous, very friable; cross-laminated on large scale; forms weak ledges	16.5
11.	Claystone: very light olive gray, shaly, gypseous throughout; forms slope	66.0
12.	Mudstone: light olive gray; contains a few thin, resistant, ripple-marked beds which form weak ledges; forms steep slope with bench at top	22.0
13.	Mudstone: light olive gray; like no. 12; forms steep slope with bench at top	44.0
14.	Mudstone: light olive gray, calcareous, gypseous; like no. 11; forms weak ledge	5.5
15.	Mudstone: light olive gray, shaly; like no. 12; contains thick (1½ ft.) structureless mudstone bed near center; forms slope	51.5
16.	Mudstone: yellowish gray to light olive gray, shaly; like no. 11; varved; contains selenite in veins and between beds; locally impregnated with gypsum; forms weak cliff; grades downward into no. 17	11.0

Total Shnabkaib member 249.5

Middle red member; units forming alternating series of slopes (dusky red and light olive-gray shaly, crumbly mudstone with selenite) and ledges (light-brown, gypseous, ripple-marked siltstone)

17. Mudstone: light brown, shaly, hard; dominant type near center of unit; alternates with:
    Claystone: dusky red, crumbly; dominant type at bottom and top of unit

Feet

Contains selenite veins throughout; contains ledge of pale to very pale orange clay-stone near top
Forms steep slope. 49.5

18. Siltstone: very light olive gray, fine-grained, very calcareous, hard; forms promi-nent light gray band at base of steep slope; forms bench. 5.0

19. Mudstone: weak reddish brown, structureless; alternates with:
Siltstone: weak reddish brown and light olive gray, structureless to shaly
Forms bench. 33.0

20. Mudstone: very light olive gray, micaceous, shaly, ripple-marked; forms con-spicuous light band along hillside; forms bench. 0.5

21. Mudstone: weak reddish brown; contains thin ledges (2–12 in.) of siltstone at wide intervals; like no. 19; forms bench. 52.0

22. Mudstone: pale reddish brown, gypseous, thin-bedded, weak; forms ledge. 2.0

23. Mudstone: dusky red, and siltstone: weak reddish brown to pale olive; like no. 19; forms slope. 10.0

24. Siltstone: very light olive gray, very gypseous; beds thin and flat; contains mud-stone bed near center; forms rim of mesa. 9.5

25. Siltstone: moderate brown and light olive gray, fine-grained; cut by selenite veins; forms cliff underlying mesa capping; bottom half locally concealed. 18.5

26. Siltstone: light olive gray, gypseous; like no. 24; forms thin ledge. 0.3

27. Mudstone: dusky red; forms slope; much concealed. 4.5

28. Siltstone: light olive gray to very pale brown, calcareous, gypseous; beds irregular; weathers solution-pitted, cavernous; forms cliff. 5.0

29. Mudstone: dusky red; like no. 27; forms slope. 10.0

30. Siltstone: light to very pale brown, gypseous, thin-bedded; like no. 22; forms weak ledge. 1.0

31. Claystone: dusky red, fissile; like no. 27; forms slope. 11.5

32. Siltstone: light olive gray, fine-grained, calcareous, shaly; like no. 24; forms ledge. .   0.5

33. Mudstone: light brown to very light olive gray; and claystone: weak reddish brown; like no. 19; forms slope. 15.0

34. Mudstone: very pale brown, thin-bedded; like no. 24; ripple-marked; forms ledge. .   1.0

35. Claystone: weak reddish brown, fissile; and mudstone: light brown, gypseous, shaly; like no. 19; forms slope. 17.0

36. Mudstone: very light olive gray, flat-bedded; like no. 24; forms weak ledge; very gypseous toward top. 3.0

37. Claystone: weak reddish brown and structureless to dusky red and fissile; and silt-stone: weak reddish brown to light olive gray; like no. 19; contains nodules of gypsum and selenite veins; forms steep slope, largely concealed in lower part, with a few weak ledges. 38.0

38. Claystone: light brown and light olive gray, silty, gypseous, shaly; locally ripple-marked; forms ledge. . . . .   1.0+

39. Mudstone: weak red to light olive gray, fissile, brittle; forms slope. . . . . . . .exposed   3.0

Total middle red member. 291.0

40. Concealed: not measured (possibly 100–300 ft.).
Beds 41–50 measured about 10 miles se. of Fredonia
Virgin limestone member:

41. Limestone: pale brown and very light olive gray, aphanitic, dolomitic; beds thin (⅛–½ in.); forms ledge. 2.0

42. Claystone: weak reddish brown, fissile, brittle; forms slope.   22.0

43. Siltstone: very light olive gray, shaly; some beds fissile; forms slope. 5.5

44. Limestone: light gray, dolomitic, resistant; beds 2–4 in. thick; contains fossils (mollusks); weathers rounded; forms ledge 2.0

Feet

45. Limestone: light olive gray, dolomitic, very silty and argillaceous, fissile; forms recess... 3.0

46. Limestone: light gray, aphanitic, dolomitic; beds rubbly, ½–2 in. thick........... 5.5

47. Limestone: light gray, aphanitic, dolomitic, resistant; beds ½–6 in. thick (2–6 in. near base); contains molds of mollusks; weathers rounded; forms ledge......... 4.5

Total Virgin limestone... 44.5
Unconformity: relief of 1–3 ft. in lateral distance of 50 ft.
Lower red member:

48. Claystone: weak reddish brown, shaly, brittle; forms slope; alternates with:
Mudstone: light brown to light gray, gypseous, crumbly; contains some very fine sand; forms ledges ½–2 ft. thick at intervals of 10–15 ft...................... 49.5+

49. Concealed: valley bottom; thickness not determined (possibly 100 ft.±)

50. Siltstone: pale reddish brown, calcareous; contains ripple marks; forms slope...... 22.0+

51. Mudstone: pale reddish brown, calcareous, shaly; forms ledge.................. 2.0

52. Mudstone: light brown, slightly calcareous, crumbly, brittle; forms slope; alternates with:
Siltstone: pale reddish brown; beds thin (1–2 in.); like no. 50; forms 3 ledges...... 18.0

53. Siltstone: pale reddish brown, calcareous, thin-bedded (½–2 in.); like no. 51; contains ripple marks; forms weak ledge; near center contains 1-ft. bed of:
Sandstone: light brown, very fine- to fine-grained, friable
Total.. 5.5

54. Claystone: weak reddish brown, fissile; forms slope; alternates with:
Mudstone: weak red; forms ledges 2–4 in. thick at intervals of 3–8 ft.
Total.. 33.0

Total lower red member.. 130.0+
Total Moenkopi measured... 888.5+
Unconformity: relief of 15 ft. in surface of Kaibab formation in horizontal distance of ¼ mi.
Kaibab formation:
Limestone: very light yellowish brown, silty; beds moderately thick (1–2 ft.); contains molluscan fauna

SECTION 34.—*Piute Farms, Utah*

Measured north of San Juan River, west of Piute Farms

Shinarump conglomerate:
Sandstone: pale brown, fine- to coarse-grained; locally contains pebbles up to 2 in.; cross laminated on small scale
Unconformity:
Undulating surface with relief of 2–3 ft. in distance of 100 yards; uppermost foot of Moenkopi claystone yellowish gray from deoxidation
Moenkopi formation:

Feet

1. Claystone: pale red, crumbly, structureless; forms long slope; includes a few thin (1–2 in.) shaly siltstone beds, resistant; one 2-ft. siltstone bed at 33 ft.; weathers reddish brown with thin green bands... 104.5

2. Siltstone: orange pink, shaly; some ripple lamination; some flat bedding; weathers to steep slope; contains thin, reddish-brown claystone forming weak zones...... 27.5

3. Siltstone: grayish orange pink; forms massive, resistant cliff; cross-laminated on a large scale at base; flat-bedded above; weathers red with white bands.......... 14.5

4. Claystone: pale red, crumbly, fissile; forms slopes; contains gypsum veins; includes thin ripple-marked siltstone beds that form ledges........................... 32.0

5. Siltstone: pale red, thin, irregularly bedded; forms weak ledge.................. 8.5

6. Mudstone: pale red; forms slope; like no. 4 but contains more silt; alternates with:
Siltstone: pale red, shaly, ripple marked
Total.. 18.5

7. Siltstone: pale red, thin, irregularly bedded; forms steep slope.................. 12.5

Feet

8. Siltstone: grayish orange pink; beds 2–3 ft. thick; structureless to cross-laminated; weathers to resistant cliff, pale reddish brown............................ 11.0

9. Claystone: pale red, structureless; in layers (2–30 in. thick) separated by thin (¼–2 in.) beds of light bluish-gray, flat to ripple-marked siltstone; includes layers of silty, pale-red, concretionary mudstone; entire unit weak; undercuts cliff or forms slope; selenite veins form network pattern........................... 77.0

10. Gypsum: white to pale red; forms cap of hill and bench; persistent for several miles.. 3.0

Total Moenkopi... 309.0

Unconformity: assumed
Cutler formation:
  Organ Rock member:
    Series of bright red, thick-bedded siltstones and mudstones
    Siltstone: light brown, thick-bedded; alternating with:
    Mudstone: pale reddish brown

SECTION 35.—*Monument Valley, Arizona*

Measured at southeast corner of Monument Valley

(Dip 2° southwest)

Shinarump conglomerate:
  Sandstone: small gravels and coarse sand; prominently cross-laminated to base; forms resistant massive cliff-capping mesa
Unconformity: surface of erosion; channels up to 5 ft. within distances of 100 ft.
Moenkopi formation:

Feet

1. Claystone: weak reddish brown with light-yellow streaks; coarse-grained, brittle; contains veins of selenite; forms slope with lower part concealed.............. 8.0

2. Sandstone: pale reddish brown, very fine-grained, thin-bedded (¼ in. thick); shows ripple lamination; contains mud curls and bed with mud balls; weathers weak reddish brown; forms resistant ledge..................................... 2.0

3. Siltstone: pale reddish brown, shaly; contains abundant large ripples; near center contains two weak ledges (2–3 ft.) of cross-laminated, ripple-marked siltstone; forms slope with upper part largely concealed............................. 50.5

4. Sandstone: very pale orange, very fine-grained; beds 1–3 ft. thick; mostly flat-bedded but cross-laminated near base; contains cusp ripple marks at base; contains mud cracks, mud pellets, and tracks of vertebrate animals; weathers moderate brown; forms massive resistant ledge................................ 16.5

5. Claystone: weak reddish brown, brittle; forms recess........................ 2.0

6. Siltstone: pale reddish brown, shaly; contains mud cracks and small current ripple marks; forms slope.. 38.5

7. Siltstone: pale reddish brown; beds thick; weakly cross-laminated on large scale; contains cusp ripple marks at top; similar to no. 4 but with thicker beds; weathers weak reddish brown; forms cliff... 7.0

8. Siltstone: pale reddish brown; like no. 6; contains current ripple marks; weathers weak reddish brown; forms slope or bench............................... 23.0

9. Sandstone: weak orange, fine-grained, hard; contains compound cross-lamination on small scale throughout; weathers light brown; forms resistant ledge.......... 1.0

10. Siltstone: pale reddish brown, sandy, slope forming; like no. 6; beds mostly ¼–½ in.; contains current ripple marks and fucoids; weathers weak reddish brown. 9.0

11. Sandstone: very pale orange, fine-grained, friable; bedding locally gnarly; weathers light brown; forms resistant ledge.. 2.0

Total Moenkopi... 159.5

Cutler formation? or basal Moenkopi formation?:
  Hoskinnini member:

Feet

1. Sandstone: pale reddish brown, very fine-grained, structureless; weathers weak reddish brown; forms slope.. 11.0

2. Sandstone: pale reddish brown, fine-grained, friable; beds thick and irregular; locally cross-laminated; forms ledge... 5.0

3. Sandstone: weak reddish brown, very fine-grained with abundant medium-sized grains scattered throughout; structureless or with gnarly beds; contains red and white quartz and some feldspar grains; like no. 1; contains pockets and lenses of light brownish sandstone near base; weathers to weak rounded cliff or steep slope... 20.0

Total thickness... 36.0

Cutler formation:
De Chelly sandstone member:
Sandstone: mostly light orange but locally white, very fine-grained; composed of quartz grains; cross-laminated on large scale with laminations beveled to even flat surface for ½ mile; weathers light brown.

SECTION 36.—*White Canyon, Utah*

Measured 4 miles northeast of Dandy Crossing

Shinarump conglomerate:
Sandstone: very pale orange, very fine-grained, resistant; beds thick (2–12 in.); contains ripple marks; locally conglomeratic with angular gravels of quartz and chert mostly ¼ in. (maximum 1 in.); weathers light brown; forms resistant ledge with straight face and sharp corners

Unconformity: assumed

Moenkopi formation:

Feet

1. Siltstone: pale reddish brown, structureless; beds thick (4–15 ft.); weathers weak reddish brown; forms resistant rounded cliff............................... 62.5

2. Siltstone: pale reddish brown, shaly; middle beds thicker, more massive; weathers weak reddish brown; forms slope... 38.5

3. Siltstone: pale reddish brown, structureless; three thick beds (10–15 ft.) separated by thin, shaly partings; weathers weak reddish brown; forms massive, resistant cliff... 57.0

4. Siltstone: pale reddish brown, shaly; contains worm borings and plant stems; contains structureless rounded mudstone at top; forms slope.................... 7.5

5. Siltstone: pale reddish brown, structureless; forms resistant ledge............... 5.5

6. Claystone: weak reddish brown, silty, crumbly; forms slope; partly concealed..... 4.5

7. Sandstone: very pale reddish brown with pale reddish-brown specks, very fine-grained; cross-laminated on large scale; forms prominent marker bed; forms steep slope.. 49.5

8. Siltstone: pale reddish brown; beds thick and locally gnarly; weathers pale reddish brown to black; forms massive cliff... 23.0

9. Siltstone: pale reddish brown, shaly; contains resistant ledges of siltstone (1–2 ft.); forms slope.. 29.0

10. Conglomerate: bed shows lensing character, thickening laterally to 6 ft. within 50 ft. sandstone bed in which conglomerate lens is developed; forms resistant ledge... 1.5
matrix: pale reddish-brown siltstone;
gravel: rounded gravels (average ⅛- ½ in.), elongate to circular, of pale reddish-brown limestone.

11.* Siltstone: pale reddish brown, structureless; like no. 3; forms cliff.............. 21.0

Total Moenkopi... 299.5

Unconformity: assumed

* This sandstone may be equivalent to Hoskinnini tongue of Cutler? formation in Monument Valley area.

Feet

Cutler formation:
  Organ Rock member:
    1. Sandstone: pale reddish brown, very fine-grained, friable; contains small sand concretion; forms rounded ledge.. 5.5
    2. Siltstone: pale reddish brown, very thin-bedded; contains worm borings and mud cracks; contains series of thin (½–2 ft.) rounded ledges of resistant siltstone at 10–20 ft. intervals; like no. 9; forms slope................................ 71.0
    3. Sandstone: pale yellow, very fine-grained; beds flat and of medium thickness (6–12 in.); forms resistant ledge 5.5
    4. Siltstone: weak reddish brown; beds very thin to medium (⅛–2 in.); contains worm borings and abundant fragments of poorly preserved plant remains; forms slope. 5.5

        Organ Rock member: Total.. 87.5
  Cedar Mesa sandstone member:
    Sandstone: massive, cross-laminated on large scale

SECTION 37.—*Bears Ears, Utah*

Measured near Highway 86, 2½ miles southwest of Maverick Spring

Shinarump conglomerate:
  Sandstone: very pale orange, mostly fine-grained but locally with small gravels, resistant; shows complex cross-lamination on medium scale to base
Unconformity: small hills (2–3 ft. high) on surface of light olive-gray claystone; depressions filled with cross-laminated sand.

Moenkopi formation:

Feet

1. Claystone: mostly pale reddish brown but locally light olive gray; contains bleached zone at top; forms slope the upper ¾ of which is largely concealed............ 120.5
2. Siltstone: pale reddish brown, silty; ripple-laminated in lower part; upper part contains cores-and-shells of mud; forms ledge................................ 3.0
3. Claystone: weak reddish brown, crumbly; like no. 1; contains fish remains; contains a few thin siltstone beds (1–3 in.); forms slope........................ 6.5
4. Siltstone: pale reddish brown, resistant; beds 1–4 ft. thick; contains track casts; contains abundant ripple laminae; weathers weak reddish brown; forms ledge... 11.0
5. Mudstone: pale reddish brown, brittle; weathers weak reddish brown; alternates with:
   Siltstone: pale reddish brown; beds thin and irregular; locally shows ripple marks; contains plant (?) impressions; weathers weak reddish brown
   Forms slope.. 33.5
6. Siltstone: very pale brown, resistant; beds 2–10 ft. thick; many beds cross-laminated on large scale, especially toward top of unit; contains bones of amphibians; basal portion contains thin parting beds of deep-brown mudstone and abundant mud pellets up to 8 in. diameter; weathers pale reddish brown to white; forms prominent cliff with upper beds forming "rock babies"........................ 57.0
7. Claystone: very pale brown, thin-bedded (½–6 in.), resistant; contains ripple marks; cross-laminated on small scale; weathers light brown; alternates with:
   Claystone: pale reddish brown, crumbly; beds 2–24 in. thick; weathers weak reddish brown
   Forms series of ledges transitional between units above and below.............. 6.0
8. Claystone: pale reddish brown, micaceous, fissile, shaly; locally contains mud cracks; weathers reddish brown; alternates with a few beds of:
   Siltstone: pale reddish brown, thin-bedded; contains mud pellets and ripple marks locally
   Forms weak slope.. 25.0
9. Siltstone: weak red; cross-laminated on large scale throughout; weathers weak reddish brown; forms resistant cliff.................................... 21.0
10. Claystone: weak reddish brown, shaly; forms slope........................ 22.0

Feet

11. Sandstone: very pale orange, fine-grained, friable; cross-laminated on medium scale; surface contains cusp ripple marks with mud cracks in troughs 2.0

Total Moenkopi 307.5
Unconformity: assumed

Cutler formation:
Organ Rock member?:
1. Sandstone: pale reddish brown, very fine-grained; forms resistant ledge with straight face; forms cap of series 11.0

2. Sandstone: pale reddish brown, predominantly fine-grained; beds 1–2 ft. thick; forms steep slope 19.0

3. Sandstone: pale reddish brown mottled with light yellowish brown (esp. near base), very fine-grained with some medium-sized, rounded grains; beds gnarly, 2–4 ft. thick; weathers locally to honeycomb surface; forms massive, rounded cliff 47.0

4. Mudstone: weak reddish brown mottled with light yellowish brown, crumbly; forms slope . . . . estimated several hundred feet.

SECTION (Partial) 38.—*Lavender Canyon, Utah*

Measured on mesa west side of canyon, 1 mile south of Indian Creek

Shinarump conglomerate:
Sandstone: coarse-grained, cross-laminated to base; contains a few scattered gravels up to 1 in. diameter; weathers brown; forms massive cliff capping mesa

Moenkopi formation:

Feet

1. Claystone: weak reddish brown, brittle, structureless; upper 2 ft. weak yellow from deoxidation; undermines beds above 6.0

2. Siltstone: weak reddish brown, shaly; contains a few thicker (½–1 ft.) beds of siltstone; contains ripple marks; contains bed with mud cores-and-shells 6 ft. above base; forms slope 37.0

3. Siltstone: weak reddish brown, structureless; forms prominent rounded cliff composed of thick (2–4 ft.) resistant beds; alternates with:
Claystone: weak reddish brown, shaly, weak; and:
Siltstone: weak yellow, shaly, weak; contains mud cracks and ripple marks
Total forms prominent cliff 24.0

4. Siltstone: pale reddish brown to yellowish gray, shaly; contains a few thicker (2–4 in.), more resistant beds of very pale brown to weak reddish-brown siltstone; contains abundant ripple marks; contains reptile tracks 10 ft. above base; forms slope 46.5

5. Limestone: very pale brown, silty, thick-bedded (½–2 ft.); weathers pale reddish brown; grades upward into:
Siltstone: weak red; contains abundant cusp ripple marks, shrinkage cracks, mud flows in several beds; weathers pale reddish brown
Forms resistant cliff 11.0

6. Siltstone: weak reddish brown; mostly thin-bedded (¼–½ in.) but locally with thicker (3–4 ft.) rounded beds; contains vertebrate animal remains in topmost bed; forms slope with base concealed . . . . exposed   32.5

Total Moenkopi exposed . . . .   157.0+
Concealed: alluvium

SECTION 39.—*Indian Creek, Utah*

Measured on north side, opposite Totem Pole

(Dip 2° north)

Shinarump conglomerate:
Sandstone: gray, coarse-grained, cross-laminated; contains conglomerate with gravels abundant but small (mostly ⅛–¼ in., up to 1 in.); 20 ft. thick where measured but absent 50 ft. to the west where Chinle marl rests on Moenkopi formation.

Feet

Unconformity: surface locally irregular; mudstone at top of Moenkopi is bleached white; apparently represents top of Moenkopi hill for Shinarump is very thin here, though 50 ft. or more thick 2 miles to east.

Moenkopi formation:

1. Siltstone: light red, shaly; 1–2 ft. beds alternate with:
   Mudstone: weak red; beds weak; 2–3 ft. thick; and a few beds of:
   Siltstone: resistant, thick-bedded (1–2 ft.); weathers rounded
   Total.. 71.5

2. Siltstone: pale reddish brown, shaly, fissile; contains abundant ripple marks; forms bench.. 16.5

3. Siltstone: pale reddish brown, structureless, resistant; weathers rounded; 1–2 ft. beds alternate with:
   Mudstone: weak red and light olive gray, brittle, crumbly; occurs as weak beds 1–3 ft. thick
   Forms weak cliff... 38.5

4. Siltstone: pale reddish brown, shaly; forms slope........................... 17.5

5. Siltstone: pale reddish brown, hard; contains several shaly parting beds; contains ripple laminations and large ripple marks; forms resistant cliff............... 8.5

6. Mudstone: weak reddish brown, with light olive-gray bands, brittle; forms slope... 16.5

7. Siltstone: weak red, structureless; similar to no. 5; forms resistant ledge......... 8.5

8. Siltstone: pale reddish brown, beds thin and flat; forms recess.................. 8.5

9. Sandstone: pale reddish brown, very fine-grained, very friable; beds 1–3 ft. thick; forms resistant rounded cliff; forms cap of mesa............................ 5.5

10. Siltstone: pale reddish brown, thin-bedded (⅛–½ in.); alternates with:
    Siltstone: resistant; beds 2–24 in.; contains abundant ripple marks and some mud cores-and-shells; forms ledges at intervals of 5–10 ft.
    Total forms slope.. 104.5

11. Siltstone: weak reddish brown and light olive gray, brittle; forms slope........... 5.5

12. Siltstone: weak reddish brown, thick-bedded; like no. 5; forms "rock babies"..... 6.0

13. Siltstone: pale reddish brown, shaly; forms slope........................... 11.0

14. Siltstone: weak red with yellowish-gray blotches, thick-bedded, resistant; like no. 5; forms "rock babies".. 11.0

15. Siltstone: pale reddish brown and yellowish gray in bands and blotches; beds irregular, mostly shaly with a few thicker (½–1 ft.) more resistant beds; locally contains many quartz aggregates; forms slope............................. 26.5

16. Siltstone: pale reddish brown; beds thick (2–4 ft.); forms resistant, massive cliff with rounded "rock babies".. 30.0

17. Siltstone: pale reddish brown, shaly; like no. 2; forms slope.................... 5.5

18. Siltstone: pale reddish brown, cross-laminated; forms weak ledge............... 3.0

19. Siltstone: pale reddish brown, shaly; contains scattered medium-sized sand grains; forms slope... 5.5

20. Conglomerate: forms resistant ledge....................................... 12.0
    matrix: weak reddish brown sandstone
    gravels: ½–1 in. (maximum 3 in.), subangular, yellow silty limestone; subordinate well-rounded gravels of quartz, flint, and other durable rocks

Total Moenkopi... 412.0

Unconformity: irregular surface with channels and hills giving relief of several feet in distance of ¼ mile

Cutler formation (Bogus tongue):
   Sandstone: weak red, locally cross-laminated on large scale; contains scattered gravels; forms resistant cliff

REFERENCES CITED

Bacon, Charles S. (1948) *Geology of the Confusion Range, west-central Utah*, Geol. Soc. Am., Bull., vol. 59, p. 1027–1052.

Baker, A. A. (1933) *Geology and oil possibilities of the Moab district, Grand and San Juan counties, Utah*, U. S. Geol. Survey, Bull. 841, 95 pages.

———— (1936) *Geology of the Monument Valley–Navajo Mountain region, San Juan County, Utah*, U. S. Geol. Survey, Bull. 865, 106 pages.

———— (1946) *Geology of the Green River Desert–Cataract Canyon region, Emery, Wayne, and Garfield counties, Utah*, U. S. Geol. Survey, Bull. 951, 122 pages.

————, Dobbins, C. E., McKnight, E. T., and Reeside, J. B., Jr. (1927) *Notes on the stratigraphy of the Moab region, Utah*, Am. Assoc. Petrol. Geol., Bull., vol. 11, p. 785–808.

———— and Reeside, J. B., Jr. (1929) *Correlation of the Permian of southern Utah, northern Arizona, northwestern New Mexico, and southwestern Colorado*, Am. Assoc. Petrol. Geol., Bull., vol. 13, p. 1413–1448.

Bates, Robert L. (1933) *The oil and gas resources of New Mexico*, N. Mex. School Mines, Bull. 18, 320 pages.

Branson, E. B. (1915) *Origin of thick salt and gypsum deposits*, Geol. Soc. Am., Bull., vol. 26, p. 231–242.

Brady, L. F. (1935) *Notes on the geology of northern Arizona, no. 2, the Moencopi sandstone*, Museum Northern Ariz., Mus. Notes, vol. 8, no. 2, p. 9–12.

———— (1947) *Invertebrate tracks from the Coconino sandstone of northern Arizona*, Jour. Paleont., vol. 21, p. 466–472.

Brown, Barnum (1933) *A new genus of Stegocephalia from the Triassic of Arizona*, Am. Mus. Novit., no. 640, p. 1–4.

Camp, C. L., Colbert, E. H., McKee, E. D., Welles, S. P. (1947) *A guide to the continental Triassic of northern Arizona*, Plateau, vol. 20, no. 1, p. 1–9.

Clarke, F. W. (1924) *Data of geochemistry*, U. S. Geol. Survey, Bull. 770, p. 219–221.

Dake, C. L. (1920) *The pre-Moenkopi (pre-Permian) unconformity of the Colorado Plateau*, Jour. Geol., vol. 28, p. 61–74.

Dane, C. H. (1935) *Geology of the Salt Valley anticline and the northwest flank of the Uncompahgre Plateau, Grand county, Utah*, U. S. Geol. Survey, Bull. 863, 184 pages.

Darton, N. H. (1910) *A reconnaissance of parts of northwestern New Mexico and northern Arizona*, U. S. Geol. Survey, Bull. 435, 88 pages.

———— (1925) *A résumé of Arizona geology*, Univ. Ariz. Bull., no. 119, 298 pages.

Daugherty, L. H. (1941) *The Upper Triassic flora of Arizona*, Carnegie Inst. Washington, Publ. 526, 108 pages.

Davis, W. M. (1903) *An excursion to the plateau province of Utah and Arizona*, Mus. Comp. Zool., Harv. Coll., Bull., vol. 52, p. 1–50.

Dutton, C. E. (1880) *Report on the geology of the high plateaus of Utah*, U. S. Geog. Geol. Survey Rocky Mountain Region, p. 1–307.

———— (1882) *Tertiary history of the Grand Canyon district*, U. S. Geol. Survey, Mon. 2, 264 pages.

Evans, O. F. (1943) *Effect of change of wave size on the size and shape of ripple marks*, Jour. Sed. Petrol., vol. 13, no. 1, p. 35–37.

Gilbert, G. K. (1875) *Report on geology of portions of Nevada, Utah, California and Arizona*, U. S. Geog. Geol. Surveys W. 100th Mer. Rept., vol. 3, p. 17–187.

———— (1880) *Geology of the Henry Mountains*, U. S. Geog. Geol. Survey Rocky Mountain Region, Sec. division, p. 1–170.

Gilluly, James (1929) *Geology and oil and gas prospects of part of the San Rafael Swell, Utah*, U. S. Geol. Survey, Bull. 806, p. 69–130.

———— and Reeside, John B., Jr. (1928) *Sedimentary rocks of San Rafael Swell and some adjacent areas in eastern Utah*, U. S. Geol. Survey, Prof. Paper 150, p. 61–110.

Glock, Waldo (1929) *Geology of the east-central part of the Spring Mountain Range, Nevada*, Am. Jour. Sci., 5th ser., vol. 17, p. 326–341.

Gregory, H. E. (1913) *The Shinarump conglomerate*, Am. Jour. Sci., 4th ser., vol. 35, p. 424–438.

———— (1914) *Reconnaissance of a portion of the Little Colorado Valley*, Am. Jour. Sci., 4th ser., vol. 38, p. 491–501.

———— (1916) *The Navajo country*, U. S. Geol. Survey, Water-Supply Paper 380, p. 1–219.

———— (1917) *Geology of the Navajo country*, U. S. Geol. Survey, Prof. Paper 93, p. 23.

———— (1938) *The San Juan country, a geographic and geologic reconnaissance of southeastern Utah*, U. S. Geol. Survey, Prof. Paper 188, 117 pages.

———— (1948) *Geology and geography of central Kane county, Utah*, Geol. Soc. Am., Bull., vol. 59, p. 211–248.

———— (1952) *The geology and geography of the Zion park region, Utah-Arizona*, U. S. Geol. Survey, Prof. Paper 220, 200 pages.

———— **and Anderson, J. C.** (1939) *Geographic and geologic sketch* of the *Capitol Reef National Monument*, Geol. Soc. Am., vol. 50, p. 1827–1850.

———— **and Moore, R. C.** (1931) *The Kaiparowits region*, U. S. Geol. Survey, Prof. Paper 164, 161 pages.

———— **and Noble, L. F.** (1923) *Notes on a geological traverse from Mohave, California, to the mouth of the San Juan River, Utah*, Am. Jour. Sci., 5th ser., vol. 5, p. 229–238.

———— **and Williams, Norman C.** (1947) *Zion National Monument, Utah*, Geol. Soc. Am., Bull., vol. 58, p. 211–244.

Hager, Dorsey (1922) *Oil possibilities of the Holbrook area in northeast Arizona*, Mining and Oil Bull., vol. 8, no. 1, p. 23–27, 33–34; no. 2, p. 71–74, 81, 94; no. 3, p. 135–140.

Hall, James (1843) *Geology of New York, Pt. IV, comprising the survey of the fourth geological district*, Albany, Carroll & Cook, 683 pages.

Hazzard, J. C. (1937) *Lower Triassic rocks in San Bernardino County, Calif.* (abstract), Geol. Soc. Am., Pr. 1936, p. 354.

Hewett, D. F. (1931) *Geology and ore-deposits of the Goodsprings quadrangle, Nevada*, U. S. Geol. Survey, Prof. Paper 162, 172 pages.

Huntington, E. and Goldthwait, J. W. (1903) *The Hurricane fault in southwestern Utah*, Jour. Geol., vol. 11, p. 46–63.

———— (1904) *The Hurricane fault in the Toquerville district, Utah*, Mus. Comp. Zool., Harv. Coll., Bull. 42, p. 199–259.

Johnson, D. W. (1938) *Shore processes and shoreline development*, John Wiley and Sons, 584 pages.

Jukes, J. B. (1872) *Student's manual of geology*, 3rd ed., Edinburgh, A. & C. Black, p. 163–164.

Kindle, E. M. (1917) *Recent and fossil ripple-mark*, Canada Dept. Mines, Geol. Survey, Mus. Bull. 25, 121 pages.

Knopf, Adolph (1918) *A geologic reconnaissance of the Inyo Range and the eastern slope of the southern Sierra Nevada, Cal.; with a section on the stratigraphy of the Inyo Range, by Edwin Kirk*, U. S. Geol. Survey, Prof. Paper 110, 130 pages.

Krynine, Paul D. (1949) *The origin of red beds*, N. Y. Acad. Sci., Tr., ser. 2, vol. 2, no. 3, p. 60–68.

Kummel, Bernhard, Jr. (1943) *The Thaynes formation, Bear Lake Valley, Idaho*, Am. Jour. Sci., vol. 241, p. 316–332.

Lee, Willis T. (1907) *The Iron County coal field, Utah*, U. S. Geol. Survey, Bull. 316, p. 359–375.

Longwell, Chester R. (1921) *Geology of the Muddy Mountains, Nevada, with a section to the Grand Wash Cliffs in western Arizona*, Am. Jour. Sci., 5th ser., vol. 1, p. 39–62.

———— (1925) *The pre-Triassic unconformity in southern Nevada*, Am. Jour. Sci., 5th ser., vol. 10, p. 93–106.

———— (1928) *Geology of the Muddy Mountains, Nevada, with a section through the Virgin Range to the Grand Wash Cliffs, Arizona*, U. S. Geol. Survey, Bull. 798, 152 pages.

———— (1949) *Structure of the northern Muddy Mountain area, Nevada*, Geol. Soc. Am., vol. 60, p. 923–968.

———— **and Others** (1923) *Rock formations in the Colorado Plateau of southern Utah and northern Arizona*, U. S. Geol. Survey, Prof. Paper 132, p. 1–25.

Marcou, Jules (1858) *Geology of North America*, Zurcher and Furrer, Zurich, p. 1–144.

Maxey, George B. (1946) *Geology of part of the Pavant Range, Millard County, Utah*, Am. Jour. Sci., vol. 244, p. 324–356.

McKee, Edwin D. (1938) *The environment and history of the Toroweap and Kaibab formations of northern Arizona and southern Utah*, Carnegie Inst. Wash., Pub. 492, 268 pages.

———— (1939) *Some types of bedding in the Colorado River delta*, Jour. Geol., vol. 47, p. 64–81.

———— (1951) *Sedimentary basins of Arizona and adjoining areas*, Geol. Soc. Am., Bull., vol. 62, p. 481–506.

———— and **Weir, Gordon W.** (1953) *Terminology for stratification and cross-stratification in sedimentary rocks*, Geol. Soc. Am., Bull., vol. 64, p. 381–390.

McKnight, E. T. (1940) *Geology of area between Green and Colorado rivers, Grand and San Juan counties, Utah*, U. S. Geol. Survey, Bull. 908, 147 pages.

Moore, R. C. (1949) *Introduction to Historical Geology*, McGraw-Hill Book Co. Inc., N. Y., 582 pages.

Muller, S. W., and Ferguson, H. G. (1939) *Mesozoic stratigraphy of the Hawthorne and Tonopah quadrangles*, Geol. Soc. Am., Bull., vol. 50, p. 1573–1624.

Newberry, J. S. (1861) *In Report upon the Colorado River of the West*, explored in 1857–58 by Lieut. J. C. Ives, Washington: Govt. Printing Office, pt. 3, Geol. Rept., 154 pages.

Newell, Norman D. and Kummel, Bernhard (1941) *Permo-Triassic Boundary in Idaho, Montana, and Wyoming*, Am. Jour. Sci., vol. 239, p. 204–208.

———— (1942) *Lower Eo-Triassic stratigraphy, western Wyoming and southeast Idaho*, Geol. Soc. Am., Bull., vol. 53, p. 937–996.

Noble, L. F. (1922) *A section of the Paleozoic formations of the Grand Canyon at the Bass trail*, U. S. Geol. Survey, Prof. Paper 131-B, p. 23–73.

Nolan, T. B. (1935) *The Gold Hill mining district, Utah*, U. S. Geol. Survey, Prof. Paper 177, 172 pages.

———— (1943) *The Basin and Range province in Utah, Nevada, and California*, U. S. Geol. Survey, Prof. Paper 197-D, p. 141–196.

Owen, David D. (1852) *Report of a geological survey of Wisconsin, Iowa, and Minnesota*, 638 pages, Phila.

Payne, Thomas G. (1942) *Stratigraphical analysis and environmental reconstruction*, Am. Assoc. Petrol. Geol., Bull., vol. 26, p. 1697–1770.

Peabody, Frank E. (1947) *Current crescents in the Triassic Moenkopi formation*, Jour. Sed. Petrol., vol. 17, no. 2, p. 73–76.

———— (1948) *Reptile and amphibian trackways from the Lower Triassic, Moenkopi formation of Arizona and Utah*, Univ. Calif. Pub., Bull., vol. 27, p. 295–468.

Pettijohn, F. J. (1950) *Sedimentary rocks*, Harper and Brothers, N. Y. 526 pages.

Poborski, Stanislaw (1953) *The Virgin formation of the St. George, Utah, area*, Plateau, vol. 25, no. 4, p. 69–79.

Powell, J. W. (1876) *Report on the geology of the eastern portion of the Uinta Mountains*, U. S. Geog. Geol. Survey Terr., 2nd division.

Price, W. E. (1949) *The Moenkopi formation at Sycamore Canyon*, Plateau, vol. 21, no. 4, p. 49–54.

Reeside, John B., Jr., and Bassler, Harvey (1922) *Stratigraphic sections in southwestern Utah and northwestern Arizona*, U. S. Geol. Survey, Prof. Paper 129-D, p. 52–77.

Robinson, H. H. (1913) *The San Franciscan volcanic field*, U. S. Geol. Survey, Prof. Paper 76, 213 pages.

Schindewolf, A. (1928) *Studien aus dem Marburger Buntsandstein III–VIII*, Senckenbergiana 10, p. 16–54.

Schuchert, C., and Dunbar, C. O. (1941) *A textbook of geology; Part II—historical geology*, John Wiley and Sons, N. Y., 4th ed., 544 pages.

Scott, W. Frank (1950) *Triassic stratigraphy in the central Wasatch Mountains, Utah* (Abstract), Geol. Soc. Am., Bull., vol. 61, p. 1530.

Sears, J. D. (1925) *Geology and oil and gas prospects of part of Moffat County, Colo., and southern Sweetwater County, Wyo.*, U. S. Geol. Survey, Bull. 751, p. 281–284.

Shimer, H. W. (1919) *Permo-Triassic of northwestern Arizona*, Geol. Soc. Am., Bull., vol. 30, p. 493–494.

Smith, J. P. (1932) *Lower Triassic ammonoids of North America*, U. S. Geol. Survey, Prof. Paper 167, 199 pages.

Stokes, W. L. (1949) *Triassic and Jurassic rocks of Utah, oil and gas possibilities of Utah*, Utah Geol. and Min. Survey, p. 79–89.

———— (1950) *Some unusual ripple marks from the Triassic of Utah*, Jour. Geol., vol. 58, p. 153–154.

Thomas, H. D. and Krueger, M. L. (1946) *Late Paleozoic and Early Mesozoic stratigraphy of Uinta Mountains, Utah*, Am. Assoc. Petrol. Geol., Bull., vol. 30, p. 1255–1293.

Twenhofel, W. H. (1939) *Principles of sedimentation*, McGraw-Hill Book Co., 610 pages.

Walcott, C. D. (1880) *The Permian and other Paleozoic groups of the Kanab Valley, Arizona*, Am. Jour. Sci., 3rd ser., vol. 20, p. 221–225.

—— (1890) *Study of a line of displacement in the Grand Canyon of the Colorado in northern Arizona*, Geol. Soc. Am., Bull., vol. 1, p. 49–64.

Ward, L. F. (1901) *Geology of the Little Colorado Valley*, Am. Jour. Sci., 4th ser., vol. 12, p. 401–413.

———— (1905) *Status of the Mesozoic floras of the United States*, U. S. Geol. Survey, Mon. 48, pt. 1, 616 pages.

Welles, S. P. (1947) *Vertebrates from the Upper Moenkopi formation of northern Arizona*, Univ. Calif. Pub., vol. 27, no. 7, p. 241–294.

Wengerd, S. A. (1950) *Triassic rocks of northwestern New Mexico and Southwestern Colorado*, Guidebook of the San Juan basin, N. M. and Colo., First Field Conf., New Mex. Geol. Soc., p. 67–75.

Williams, J. S. (1945) *Nomenclature of Triassic rocks in northeastern Utah*, Am. Jour. Sci., vol. 243, p. 473–479.

Zo Bell, C. E. (1946) *Studies on redox potential of marine sediments*, Am. Assoc. Petrol. Geol., Bull., vol. 30, p. 477–513.

INDEX

Date Due